EX
LIBRIS   *Alison J. L. Nugent*

WILD FLOWERS
MONTH BY MONTH

Charlock.

WILD FLOWERS

MONTH BY MONTH
IN THEIR NATURAL HAUNTS

BY

EDWARD STEP, F.L.S.

AUTHOR OF "WAYSIDE AND WOODLAND BLOSSOMS"
"WAYSIDE AND WOODLAND TREES" ETC.

VOL. II.

WITH ONE HUNDRED AND SEVENTY-SIX ILLUSTRATIONS
REPRODUCED FROM ORIGINAL PHOTOGRAPHS BY THE AUTHOR
AND SIX PLATES FROM PHOTOGRAPHS IN COLOUR
BY THOMAS BADDELEY

LONDON
FREDERICK WARNE & CO. LTD.
AND NEW YORK

Printed by
MORRISON & GIBB LIMITED
Edinburgh

CONTENTS

Contents

Wild Pansy.

A Chalk-Hill Path.

JUNE ON THE CHALK-HILLS.

THIS morning we repeat one of our old walks to the
Downs, but so quickly do things come on at this
season that we shall find everything changed in aspect,
and many plants now in flower whose beginnings in some
cases we never noticed. Look at this cornfield, for example ;
on our last visit we noted the springing corn, but the most
striking thing here was Buxbaum's Speedwell (*Veronica
buxbaumii*), that covered all the ground between the wheat
plants. Now the wheat is almost hidden in the thick crop
of Charlock (*Brassica sinapistrum*), which has grown up
without being wanted and turned the field to gold. There
is another flower fairly conspicuous among the gold—the
Field Poppy (*Papaver rhœas*), which, however, will be much
more striking in another month, when Charlock will be on
the wane. Till then, when it will be in its prime, we will
leave consideration of it.

II.—B

There is another and smaller plant among the numerous constituents of the field to which we must pay some attention, because at a later date it may be obscured by the abundant weeds of greater stature. There is little need to tell you it is the Wild Pansy (*Viola tricolor*), because, though its flowers are so very small, it yet bears considerable resemblance to the smaller of the garden Pansies—or Violas as they are now called, to distinguish them from the huge newer varieties. When it is said that the flowers are very small we are speaking particularly of those before us. As a matter of fact the Pansy is more variable than most of our wild plants, especially as regards the size and colour of its flowers. Botanists have, in consequence, divided it into several permanent varieties or sub-species—some call them distinct species. Those before us do not measure quite half an inch across the flowers; the sepals are longer than the petals, and of a dark indigo-blue colour; the upper pair of petals are deep purple, the lower pair white faintly tinged with purple, and the odd lowest one bright yellow streaked with fine purple lines. Sometimes the sepals are green, and all the petals white. Observe how different the leaves are from those of other Violets: instead of the more or less heart-shapes of these we have here a rather oblong leaf, and instead of the small teeth of the margin, prevailing among other *Violas*, the Pansy leaf has broad rounded teeth, approaching to lobes. Then, look at the stipules— those ragged green scales at the base of the leaf-stalk in other *Violas*—here they are large enough to pass for leaves, and probably most persons other than botanists so regard them. They may be distinguished from the Pansy's real leaves by being cut up into slender lobes from each side almost to the middle. Another feature in which the Pansy differs from the Violets is in the non-production of those late flowers that never open, but by which the seeds are mostly produced. The Pansy has no *cleistogene* flowers, but produces its seed capsules as sequels to the ordinary

Rest Harrow,

flowers. The Wild Pansy is an annual; the Violets are perennial.

There are White Campions (*Lychnis alba*) in plenty among the corn, but as nearly all the flowers are closed they do not appear very attractive. Both leaves and flowers are very similar to those of its close relation, the Red Campion (*Lychnis dioica*), though the flowers are larger. Its present dishevelled condition is due to the fact that it opens its fresh flowers in the evening for the purpose of attracting night-flying moths, for which purpose it also pours out its fragrance. By the morning such flowers as have been fertilised hang their petals in a very limp and dejected manner; but this evening, if you came this way, you would be surprised at the wide-awake aspect of the plant. Here is a flower that is distinctly pale pink, and sometimes we may find it quite red, giving colour not only to its blossoms but also to the contention of those who say that at most it is only a sub-species of the Red Campion.

We pass the cornfield, and the footpath now runs between a copse and an open stretch of rough land, locally reputed to be public property, but the adjoining landowner has lately stretched short lengths of barbed wire across it, which we take to be a preliminary step to enclosing it. At present we will assume that local tradition is right, and walk over the land, for it is crowded with interesting things, though all have not yet reached the flowering stage. Here is Lamb's-tongue Plantain (*Plantago media*), its seedstalks, with those of its larger relative the Waybread (*Plantago major*), well known as a food for cage-birds, but its flowers much less familiar. But though these appear to be almost akin to the grasses in their simplicity, and the absence of showy petals, they have a quiet grace and beauty of their own, chiefly due to their stamens. These have white anthers which stand far out from the small corollas, supported on long slender filaments. There are two forms of the plant: one having a long flower-stalk and white filaments to the stamens; the other with a much shorter stalk and pink filaments. The plant before us, you see, is the second form. The Lamb's-tongue is a plant one gets too frequently in the lawn, where it not only spoils the uniformity of the turf, but actually kills the grass around its stout root-stock by laying its thick broad leaves in a rosette pressed so close to the ground that the grass has no chance.

These flowers are clearly built for wind-fertilisation, but it looks as though they were trying to become insect-fertilised. They produce no honey, but there is a faint fragrance which may attract insects, and the modest colour effects of pink and white make it inviting, and there is always the reward of pollen for the bee that expected honey. Anyway, that stout-bodied Humble-bee (*Bombus terrestris*) is rifling this spike of its pollen, now that he has found there is no honey, and this particular species of bee regularly visits the Lamb's-tongue flowers.

This plant before us with yellow flowers is a most annoying one. It is the Goat's-beard, or John-go-to-bed-at-noon (*Tragopogon pratensis*), and for several years, since living in a district where it is not uncommon, we have contemplated getting its portrait; but when we have had the camera with us, John has already retired for the day. It has eluded us once more, for, as you see, the long bracts from below the flower-head have closed up, and there is little of it to be seen. It is supposed to be a plant of very regular habits, and it is said that labourers in rural places always regulate their dinner-hour by watching for the closing of the Goat's-beard. We have never made inquiries of the labourer himself as to the correctness of this statement; but we know, from our observations of the plant, that if Hodge does so rely upon it, Mrs. Hodge must have rather a trying time in the preparation of his dinner. When he works in a distant field, and carries his dinner with him after breakfast, the matter would work out all right; but when he goes home to his mid-day meal and takes his cue from the closing of the Goat's-beard he must often find his wife unprepared. We have found John's shutters up at ten o'clock in the morning. Just imagine the feelings of an orderly housewife whose husband appeared for dinner at that hour! The truth of the matter appears to be that, like many other flowers, this one closes up as soon as the work of fertilisation has been completed; and, seeing that the flower-heads are expanded as early as 4 a.m., this result is usually attained before noon. John-go-to-bed, etc., is a Composite plant, like Dandelion, for which its yellow flower-heads are probably often mistaken, though the plant as a whole could not be. Instead of the broad, jag-toothed leaves of Dandelion, those of the Goat's-beard, starting from the root-stock fairly broad, narrow upwards until they look like the leaves of some coarse grass. Then, instead of the several rows of overlapping bracts which envelop the flower-head below in Dandelion, John has only one row of them, and those in the form most plentiful in this country are much longer than the flower-rays. So that when the head is closed it is a long, tapering, steeple-shaped affair, just as you see before you. After the flower-head is fertilised a seed-globe or "puff" is formed as in the case of Dandelion, but we think it is a more beautiful one than that of the Dandelion. On a later day we shall probably come across a well-developed example; but it is too soon yet.

This vigorous plant that trails its hairy stems along the ground, and puts out large, rosy, pea-shaped flowers at intervals, is the Rest Harrow (*Ononis repens*). The broad upper petal—usually called the "standard" in flowers of this type—is finely streaked with red. The leaves are divided up into three leaflets, with toothed edges and covered with sticky hairs. The stickiness is due to a secretion which has a very unpleasant odour. The plant belongs to the Pea and Bean family, and like most of its relations evidently has valuable qualities considered as

forage, and the unpleasant odour and clamminess are explained by this fact: they are thus protected against
extinction by herbivorous animals. There are really two
forms or sub-species: this prostrate form, and an erect-
growing form (*Ononis spinosa*) which is without the
objectionable-smelling sticky hairs, but has sharp spines
instead. It may be presumed that the taller-growing form
would be more liable to attack by the larger quadrupeds, to
whom the spines would act as a deterrent. Against smaller
creatures some other protection for a trailing plant would be
necessary, because they could nibble the leaves and stems in
spite of the spines. Therefore the low-growing form seeks
safety by secreting this unpleasant and fœtid clamminess.
That is a good illustration of how a plant has power to adapt
itself to varied circumstances and conditions of growth.

It is to be feared that the Rest-Harrow's flowers are
somewhat in the nature of a fraud. The mechanism—
common to most of the Leguminous plants—for dusting the
bee's underside with pollen, and afterwards getting that
pollen detached by the pistil of another flower of the same
species, is there complete. The bright colour of the petals
is of a character to attract, and to raise hopes of honey.
There are even streaks of deeper colour pointing to the
opening of the flower, but—there is no honey! Müller, who
has had the plant under observation, declares that the male
bees—who are simply seeking personal enjoyment—go away
in a temper when they discover how they have been fooled;
but that the more philosophical females, who are concerned
with the feeding of the young, at once set to work
collecting pollen, so that their visit shall not be entirely
unremunerative.

. The banks alongside this part of the path are partly
covered with a very dwarf shrub, with short prostrate
stems and small shiny leaves in pairs. These were very
noticeable on account of their rich dark green until a few
days ago. Now the leaves are almost hidden by the great

Rock Rose.

numbers of comparatively large yellow flowers. These are about the same size as Buttercups, and though they open wide and flat, their size and colour cause them often to be reckoned as some kind of Buttercup. They are really the Rock Rose (*Helianthemum chamæcistus*); and those who are not satisfied with a mere cursory glance at the things they meet with in their rambles would never be deceived into the belief that they were flowers of any species of *Ranunculus*. They lack the varnish and the stiffness of the Buttercup's petals. These are not glossy, and they are often crumpled and have the appearance of being soft in texture. Then their stamens, instead of being set out in a circlet round the broad head of carpels, are here united below, and form a crowded group close round the single pistil. That is, when at rest; touch them with a grass-bent, and the anthers move apart. You see the purpose of this? The flowers are what are termed homogamous: that is, both stamens and pistil mature simultaneously. By the crowding of the anthers to the centre they form a convenient perch upon which a bee may alight; but his touch causes them to separate, so that in his search for the honey that is not there the ripe stigmas will come in contact with the bee's head upon which there is pollen brought from another flower. Note how the unopened buds all hang their heads, as though the plant were faint for want of moisture.

Do you see those stately, but sombre, plants standing like sentinels at intervals on the waste, and towering over the smaller growths? They are merely thick flower-stems whose upper half is densely covered with stalkless flowers. The whole plant is of a uniform yellow-brown colour, and there is not a single leaf upon it. The nearest approach to leaves are the long, narrow, withered-looking scales that are pressed to the stem. These singular plants are Broomrapes, and they are related to the Toothwort (*Lathræa squamaria*) that we found in March (see Vol. I., page 21). There are two species of Broomrape here—the Greater Broomrape (*Oro-*

banche major), and the Tall Broomrape (*Orobanche elatior*), and we will secure a portrait of each. In one respect they are admirable subjects for the camera—their stems are so thick and stiff that the ordinary breeze, always blowing on the Downs, has no effect upon them. On the other side of the account there is so little variety in their dull hues that they cannot be expected to yield altogether satisfactory results.

The Broomrapes all share the bad character of the Toothwort—they are root parasites, that remind one of the people we sometimes read of in the police-court records, who get their supply of gas or electricity by tapping the pipes or wires before they pass into the meters, and thus get their supply for nothing—until found out. These parasitical plants are in a way worse than these human parasites, for even detection does not stop their malpractices, nor do they get punished. The victims of the Greater Broomrape are chiefly Furze and Broom, whilst the Tall Broomrape—

Great Broomrape

Tall Broomrape.

which is probably only a variety or sub-species of the other
—attacks the roots of the Hard-heads (*Centaurea scabiosa*),
whose long pinnate leaves you can see lying all around.
This, you will understand from what we said of the Toothwort, explains why they do not put forth a single leaf, nor
show any particle of green colour.

The Greater Broomrape is more distinctly brown than
the other, which has a decided yellow element in its
coloration. The Tall Broomrape also has its upper lip
deeply notched; but the other differences between the two
are small, and only such as one would regard as varietal,
probably due to the difference in the hosts they have
billeted themselves upon. For the greater part of the year
they remain en-
tirely out of sight,
hidden in the
ground, and not
till June do they
appear in public.
Then the growth
of the flower-stem
is rapid, and they
are in evidence, in
a fresh condition,
until August, by
which time they
have ripened their
seeds. Their dry
stems, of course,
may be found
right into the
winter.

A bird has just
flown up from
that tuft of long
grass under the

Nest of Corn-Bunting.

II.—C

rose-bush, and it looked like one of the Buntings. Yes, and here is the nest from which she arose — rather a carelessly-made structure of dry grass and rootlets, and containing two eggs only. These are whitish in their ground-colour, blotched with grey, and "scribbled" over with dark-brown in the manner characteristic of the Buntings. So far as we could take note of her form and plumage we should say it was the Corn-Bunting (*Emberiza miliaria*), which likes to make her nest in the neighbourhood of corn-lands.

Among the grass there is a little blue flower of peculiar appearance; at first sight similar to the Climbing Corydalis we met with in the woods the other day, but the habit of this plant is very different. It is the Milkwort (*Polygala vulgaris*), so-called because it was believed that cows that grazed where this plant grew, and who would eat it with the grass, would give a much greater supply of milk than usual. Although it is a perennial plant, it escapes notice among the grass when it is not in flower. The wiry stems spreading in various directions are clothed with two rows of neat lance-shaped leaves. The few small flowers are at the extremity of the stem. These flowers are not always of the same tint. They may be dark or light blue, lilac, pink, or white. Their structure is so peculiar that it is worth while pulling one to pieces carefully in order to understand it properly. There are five sepals, but the three outer of these are quite small and green, whilst the two inner ones are six times the size and coloured like petals. The petals unite to form a tube in which lie the eight stamens whose filaments also form a sheath united to the petals. At the mouth of the corolla tube there are two little bunches of fringe, the object of which is not apparent, unless it serves, like the hairs within the tube, to keep out minute honey-stealers. The pistil ends in a spoon-shaped stigma, and at the mouth of the staminal tube there is a gland which secretes a viscid fluid. When an insect inserts its tongue

Field Bindweed.

in seeking for honey, it is bound to get it smeared with
this secretion, so that, when the tongue is withdrawn past
the anthers, pollen grains adhere to it, and on being thrust
into another flower some of these are left upon the stigma.
That these arrangements are all intended to make use of
insects for cross-fertilisation is further shown by the peculiar
behaviour of the two large sepals. When fertilisation has
been effected these turn green, as though to let insects know

Milkwort.

at a glance that they need not trouble to look inside the
flower.

Our path takes us alongside another cornfield now, and
between the wheat-stems we can see many a small plant.
There are innumerable Wild Pansies, there is the pretty
little Basil Thyme (*Calamintha acinos*) not yet in flower,
and, most striking of all, there is the Field Bindweed or
Convolvulus (*Convolvulus arvensis*), a near relation of the
Hedge Bindweed we were photographing in the lane a few

days ago. This is a much smaller plant, with flowers only half the size of the other, and of a pale pink with deeper streaks. The stems mostly trail along the ground, but here and there one climbs by twining round a wheat-stalk. The calyx is not hidden by the two large hood-like bracts that we saw in Hedge Bindweed. There are two bracts here also, but they are quite small and slender, and at a little distance from the flower. Another point of difference is evident to our sense of smell, for a sweet odour like that of Furze and Bean-flowers arises from the Field Bindweed.

What we said of the troublesome nature of the long underground stems of the Hedge Bindweed applies with at least equal force to this, which indeed is a greater nuisance, because it puts in an appearance in the garden much more frequently, and is put out with great difficulty. After a good soaking rain, if one pulls steadily at a cluster of Bindweed shoots that have made their appearance above ground, it is an easy matter to haul up a length of a couple of yards of the white, spirally-coiled, underground stem; and then the broken end shows you that sufficient is left in the ground to continue the species.

Whilst the Field Convolvulus is one of our most plentiful and troublesome weeds, it is also to be numbered among the most beautiful. The decorative artist and designer have not been slow to avail themselves of this fact, and the plant, more or less conventionally treated, has been widely used for decorative purposes. Insects, too, are attracted by its scent, and we may frequently see both bees and butterflies drinking its store of nectar. To get at this in the bottom of the funnel, their tongues have to be pushed down between the stamens, and so they get covered with pollen. As the stigmas rise up between, and spread out above the stamens, the insect comes in contact with them first, and will probably leave on them some of the pollen brought from another flower. But bees and butterflies are not the only insects that benefit by the flower. See these little creatures that

Traveller's Joy.

Deadly Nightshade.

creep and fly over the flowers—so minute as scarcely to be noticed until your attention is drawn to them. They are Thrips, insects with four narrow, hairy wings, that often trouble the gardener by piercing the tissues of his greenhouse flowers and causing them to be spotty and withered. They are chiefly after honey here, for they are among the insects against which many flowers guard by developing barriers of hairs. They appear quite plainly on the focussing screen, in spite of their minuteness, and it is probable that they will appear in the photograph.

There are other things in that photograph beyond what we set out to take. There are some heads of White Clover blossoms (*Trifolium repens*). Do you notice how some of the flowers stand up whilst others hang downwards? "Thereby hangs a tale." The White Clover has so nicely adapted its flowers to the tongue of the Hive Bee (*Apis mellifica*) that it, almost alone among insects, can avail itself of the plentiful honey and at the same time return the benefit by fertilising the flower. The Hive Bee is one of the most industrious insects, and is consequently economical where its time is concerned; and it looks as though there were some kind of understanding between plant and insect, for when a flower has been cleared of its honey, and fertilised, that flower hangs down, and the bee has no occasion to waste its time in a fruitless examination of it. When White Clover is grown experimentally under a net, to exclude the bees, it yields scarcely a seed.

Turning off into the ancient lane that runs along the Downs, and is now a mere path between woods, next a track across short turf and between bushes of Juniper and ancient Yews, and then again a hedged-in lane—we come face to face with a Partridge (*Perdix cinerea*) sitting close against the roots of an Oak not a foot from the actual foottrack. Her eyes are fixed upon us, at first watching our behaviour to see if we can distinguish her from a mere heap of dead leaves and weeds. Satisfied that she has been detected, she rises with a loud clattering whir and so discloses a nest with ten eggs. Partridges do not appear to be at all particular where they make their nests. We have several times come across them, also covies of their young chicks hereabout, but this one could scarcely be in a more public position. It may be presumed that when she leaves her nest less hurriedly she partially covers the eggs with a few dead leaves, but the number of her own striking

Nest of Partridge.

feathers arranged about it is sufficient to attract attention. We should have liked to have had her portrait sitting, but as she would not stay we must content ourselves with a photo of the nest and eggs.

See how the Wild Clematis, or Traveller's Joy (*Clematis vitalba*), whose earliest shoots we took note of, is now not only spreading wide its compound leaves, but has put forth its greenish-white flowers also. Found only in the middle and southern parts of our island, the Traveller's Joy shows a

Viper's Bugloss.

special fondness for chalk soils, and all about these hills you will find the hedges heavily draped with it, and the thickets and even solitary trees on the open Downs bear great lengths of its ropy stems, and are whitened with its abundant scented flowers. But though the flowers are scented they produce no honey. The only insects that appear to be deluded by the fragrance are certain flies, and it is probable that they find their reward in a feast of pollen, of which plenty is produced by the numerous stamens. It appears to be not unlikely that Traveller's Joy is on its way to becoming a wind-fertilised plant. The feathery stigmas are of the type one finds in some *anemophilous* flowers, the feathering being calculated to catch wind-borne pollen easily. It has given up the production of honey and has sacrificed its petals, making its four downy sepals serve instead. After the sepals and stamens have been shed the fertilised stigmas increase in size, and the head of fruits with these long plumes attached becomes known as the Old Man's Beard, and remains upon the plant until spring.

The Traveller's Joy is not a spiral twiner, nor has it any tendrils, but it will climb to a height of fifteen feet by an ingenious method. Each of the three or five leaflets into which the leaf is broken up has a foot-stalk, and these foot-stalks make a single coil around any available twig, and then harden so that they can support and pull up a considerable weight of woody stem. We read of the bush-ropes that hang from the trees in tropical forests, but in a small way we have a bush-rope in this country. On the top of the Downs in winter you may often see great lengths of Traveller's Joy stems hanging from far up the old Yews, and varying in thickness from a light cord to the circumference of a man's arm. They have been carried up as thin shoots by the aid of these weak leaflet stalks, which have continued to support them after they have grown to a considerable thickness and weight.

In our earlier rambles over the Downs we have frequently

met with the Deadly Nightshade (*Atropa belladonna*), but then it was only in the form of thick shoots breaking out from the old fleshy, creeping root-stock. To-day it has reached a height between three and four feet, and its many thick stems look substantial enough to have been the growth of years. But though it appears so shrubby it is only a herb, and when winter comes these stems will be all lifeless and

hollow, and the retreats of Earwigs and Woodlice. At present they are clothed in large oval leaves, and here and there from the forking of the twigs and the axils of the leaves there droop the greenish-

Deadly Nightshade Berries.

purple bell-shaped flowers. This plant against the fence, that we are about to photograph, is an old acquaintance of ours which we have known for about fifteen years, and it is presumably very much older than that. Its leaves are always much perforated as though riddled by

Yellow-Wort.

small shot, but we believe such holes are the work of some small beetle, though we have never actually found the insect at work. Later on these flowers will be succeeded by shining black berries as big as cherries. All parts of the plant abound in *Atropin*, which has important uses in medicine but is poisonous in large doses. Care should be taken even in breaking off a sprig for examination, as the juice from a severed shoot or a bruised leaf has power to act through any slight abrasion of the skin, quickly causing dilation of the pupils of the eyes, with consequent obscurity of vision. More liberally introduced into the system it produces delirium and other troubles, and in larger doses may have fatal results.

The Dropwort (*Spiræa filipendula*), nearest relation to the Meadow-sweet (*Spiræa ulmaria*), is almost out, and already has a pretty appearance, its curved flower-stems with its crimson streaked buds rising above the handsome pinnate leaves. We shall probably meet with it again when fully out. The Yellow or Biting Stonecrop (*Sedum acre*), so familiar on rockwork in gardens, has put out a few of its golden stars, and these will soon be so crowded that it will gild great patches of the driest banks.

Here we are again at the thicket where we found the Jews'-ears on the old Elders. The Elders (*Sambucus nigra*) bear great numbers of the large flat masses of creamy-white flowers—some of them half a foot across, their flowers giving out an unpleasant odour. The rough broken ground is now thickly covered with tall rough plants, among which we cannot fail to be struck by the Viper's Bugloss (*Echium vulgare*), whose flowers are arranged somewhat after the manner of those of the Forget-me-not, only instead of a few racemes the Viper's Bugloss has scores, and they are given off all up the higher part of the stem. At present they have just begun to open the lowest bud on each raceme, and they present a striking appearance, for the buds are purplish-red whilst the open flowers are blue. It is a plant that is fond of dry soils, especially chalk, and its erect stems, three or four feet in height, with their abundant bright flowers, may usually be found in large colonies. It is often associated, as here, with the Hound's-tongue (*Cynoglossum officinale*), with dull purple flowers. The Viper's Bugloss is one of the flowers beloved of the Humming-Bird Hawk Moth (*Macroglossa stellatarum*) which fertilises it.

Steady there! Mind where you are putting your feet. That bird that flew off so quietly was a Nightjar (*Caprimulgus europæa*), and if we look about under that Furze-bush we may find her eggs. Caution is needed, for she makes no nest, and you might easily suppose her two eggs are merely bits of flint or chalk such as strew the surface hereabouts. Here they are, their white ground-colour almost hidden by clouds and veins of ashen-grey, over which are spots and blotches of purplish-brown. We should like to have photographed the bird as she sat, but she evidently thought it was safer to leave her eggs uncovered, trusting that on the bare earth they might pass for stones. Whether the bird has any knowledge of this likeness or not, it undoubtedly exists, and it is not too much to say that the prevalence of Nightjars in this country is largely due to this protective coloration of the egg. The bird itself is protectively coloured, and when it sits motionless in the sun, as it is so fond of doing, it might well be passed for a broken piece of a tree branch spotted with lichen. Its general appearance and mode of flight are so hawk-like that most keepers will shoot it as a bird of prey whose existence threatens their young Pheasants. The farmer, too, has a grudge against it, in the belief that it milks his cows and infects them with disease. As a matter of natural history, as opposed to legend, it may be said that the Nightjar's food consists entirely of insects, chiefly moths and beetles, and when his weird churring note is heard at twilight he is then industriously engulfing them in his roomy gullet.

The little plant whose neat and prim appearance is

Late Spider Orchis.

attracting your attention is the Yellow-wort (*Blackstonia perfoliata*), one of a neat and trim family—the Gentians. Its grey-green or glaucous tinted leaves are given off in pairs, and the lower edges of each pair are united, or what botanists term *connate*; the stem appearing to pass through this double leaf is said to be *perfoliate*. The funnel-shaped flower is bright yellow, and instead of falling off when faded

Eggs of Nightjar.

it remains so long that the expansion of the seed-vessel splits it up. It is useless to look for this flower on a dull day; when the sun is not shining the flowers are all closed.

Whilst we have been talking we have worked our way to the edge of the hills, and now are on the brow of the escarpment, above the huge chalk quarry, where the men with their horses and carts below us look little bigger than ants. The dark tufts of vegetation far down the slope are

really fair-sized Junipers (*Juniperus communis*) and small
Yews (*Taxus baccata*). Who shall say from this distance
what else there is? We know in a general way, from what
we have encountered on our walk, that being chalk it is sure
to be covered by a variety of interesting and beautiful things;
and we may reasonably expect to find, as we descend by the
slope that half-circles the great quarry, several plants beyond
those we have already met with. We have come across
many plants of Mullein on our way, but as these were not
yet in flower we did not dwell upon the fact. Here, however, is one whose spike of flowers is well out; but, unfortunately, the high bank on which it stands is behind a fence,
and we cannot get very near to it. However, we will take a
shot at it, and hope later to come upon as good a specimen
where we can set up the camera near enough to get a part
of the tall flower-spike, natural size or approaching it.

We have five or six species of Mullein, and no fewer than
three of them occur in this district, but the species before us
is the Dark Mullein (*Verbascum nigrum*), not that it is black
as the Latin name indicates, but that it is dark in comparison
with the whitish felt-like leaves of the Great Mullein
(*Verbascum thapsus*). The Dark Mullein, before it has
begun to flower, is often grubbed up for transference to
the garden, under the supposition that it is the Foxglove, one
of many mistakes of a similar character made by people who
will not take a little trouble to observe the common objects
of the country. The mistake in this instance arises from a
slight resemblance between the large leaves of the two
species—which, by the way, are both members of the same
family. The flowers of the Dark Mullein are yellow, and of
the type of structure known as rotate. They have a short
corolla tube, with five spreading lobes corresponding to the
petals of which the flower was formerly composed. They
are crowded on a long flower-stem which is three feet in
height, and a half of that length is covered closely with the
flowers on short foot-stalks. It is therefore not a spike, but

a raceme, the foot-stalks constituting the difference between the two forms of inflorescence. There are five stamens, and their filaments are covered with short hairs, which in this species are purple. This may appear a small point, but it is

Dark Mullein.

an important aid in identification, for only one other British species—the rare Moth Mullein (*Verbascum blattaria*)—has these hairs purple, in the other species they are white. One of these days as we ramble in this district we shall come across banks where the Dark Mullein and the Great Mullein are growing in crowds, and then you will say that the person who was disappointed in getting Mullein instead of Foxglove had no great reason for regret. Their beauty is of a different order, but they are both grand plants.

And now look around among the lowly plants, for we are on ground where several Orchids grow, and we may be so fortunate as to come across more than one species, and those different from others we have found. These elevated grassy slopes are just the places beloved of the Bee Orchis (*Ophrys apifera*); and that looks like one about a dozen yards ahead. Not one but six or seven. Until it is in flower the Bee Orchis does not arrest attention, for unlike the Early Purple and the Spotted Orchids the leaf is not blotched. We mention this point, because in the Spring, in Covent Garden Market and elsewhere, orchid plants with spotted leaves are offered for sale as Bee Orchis and Fly Orchis, but the plants so labelled are Spotted Orchis (*Orchis maculata*). If our Wild Orchids are to be grubbed up to be put upon the market, it is better that the more plentiful Spotted Orchis should be the victim, but it is a pity that ignorance of our native flora should make it so easy to impose on the public.

The Bee Orchis has uniformly green leaves of rather oblong shape, and quite short by comparison with those of the Spotted Orchis. From the centre of the leaves rises the flower-stem, usually to the length of a foot. It has only a few flowers, and of these only two or three are open at a time. Our ancestors were certainly justified in the name they bestowed on this Orchid, though the same cannot be said with respect to all the species. The forms and colours of various parts of the flower give it a remarkable resemblance to a Humble-bee at rest. The three sepals are coloured pale pink or lilac, the two lateral ones forming wings for the feigned insect. The two small petals simulate antennæ, and the broad lip takes a convex form which serves well for the body of the bee, and the resemblance is further helped by

Fragrant Orchis.

a furry protuberance on each side which might be its hairy thighs, and by a curved point which might be a protruded sting. This body is of a brown-purple colour, spotted with orange. There is no hollow spur, no honey, and nothing to suggest that the visits of bees or other insects are desired. The pollen-masses, on the contrary, are so arranged that they fall over and fertilise the stigma. The likeness between the flower and a bee has been considered at different times to indicate (*a*) that bees are welcome (the flower being a decoy), and (*b*) that the bee is not wanted, the presence of the pseudo-bee denoting that the flower is already engaged. Regarded in the light of the self-fertilising machinery, if the counterfeit present-ment means anything it must be a deterrent. But it is not clear that the likeness is anything but a fortuitous one, like the

Bee Orchis.

Swans and Doves and other resemblances seen in tropical species.

Ophrys apifera takes two forms, which are by some

authorities regarded as two sub-species; by others as distinct species. We have been looking at the typical form—the true Bee Orchis. By a piece of good fortune we now come across the other form, known as the Late Spider Orchis (*Ophrys arachnites*), which is rare and said to occur only in the counties of Surrey and Kent. It is called the *Late Spider* because there is another Spider Orchis (*Ophrys aranifera*) which flowers a month or two earlier. You will see by a comparison of the examples before us that the upper sepal is proportionately longer in the Late Spider than in the Bee, that the petals are narrower, and that the lip is marked more after the manner of a Spider's decoration. It is said that in this form the pollen-masses do not fall upon the stigma as in the other; but we have not had the necessary opportunities for testing this.

There is another Orchid here, and a more plentiful one, for as we survey the falling slope before us we can see a number of specimens without searching for them. This is the Fragrant Orchis (*Habenaria conopsea*), whose spike is crowded with rather small flowers of a crimson tint in some plants and of a more purplish-red in others; occasionally one may be found with white blossoms. Do not be deceived by the different lengths of the spike into supposing these before us are of different species. Here are two specimens close together which we will photograph, and one has about forty blossoms upon it whilst the other has less than twenty. You will notice in these flowers that, whilst the general characters of the family are retained, the lateral sepals are comparatively long and slender, the three-lobed lip is as broad as it is long, and the spur is exceedingly long and very slender. So fine and long is it that only butterflies and moths can get their proboscis into it. Look there! A moth, with wings vibrating so rapidly that they give the impression of nothing more tangible than a halo, is hovering in front of the spike. He settles on one of the flowers and inserts the long trunk that had been tightly coiled up whilst

II. *Pl.* 12.   *D* 24.

Large Butterfly Orchis.

he flew. The shining metallic mark on each fore-wing shows him to be the beautiful, though common, Silver Y-moth. He has been attracted by the fragrance of the flowers, but it is to be feared· that he will not stay long enough to let us get another photograph showing him enjoying himself. No! Gone! Did you note that he took with him the two yellow pollen-masses glued to his head. He could not get away without them, so that when he alights on another flower higher up the slope he will unfailingly leave some of the pollen on the stigma.

Ah! you may well open your eyes in admiration at our next find, if you have never seen the Large Butterfly Orchis (*Habenaria chloroleuca*). It stands about a foot and a half in height, with just a couple of broad oval leaves at its base, and about five-and-twenty inch-long flowers on the upper part of the stem, so disposed as to look like a number of white moths fluttering around it. It is also very fragrant in the evening, for it is fertilised by moths, which alone can reach to the bottom of the very long spur. There is a sub-species known as the Lesser Butterfly Orchis (*Habenaria bifolia*), with smaller flowers and narrower sepals, and the spur borne more horizontally. It is later coming into flower, and is fertilised by other species of moths.

There is a fine flower blooming just now in the mountain pastures of the north and west, but we are too far south to have a chance of seeing it, except occasionally in gardens. This is the Mountain Globe Flower (*Trollius europœus*), with much-cut palmate leaves suggestive of the Hellebores, and a fine large pale yellow flower which you might imagine to be a greatly developed Marsh Marigold. But the Globe-flower retains its spherical shape, and is composed of a larger number of coloured sepals which hide the small oblong petals. It must be a fine sight to see it flowering in its natural habitat.

All the time we have been talking about Orchids and Globe-flowers we have been somewhat quickly descending

II.—E

the steep slopes, and here we are but a short distance above the main road. Let us keep above it, and return home by crossing the meadows at the foot of the hill, and following the river so far as it goes our way.

The Chalk Quarry.

Jack-by-the-Hedge.

The River and the Meadows.

JUNE BY THE RIVER.

THE grass in the meadows is getting long for the reapers, and now is a favourable time for those who wish to get an acquaintance with the numerous kinds of grass, for many of them are in flower, and a fair percentage of the native species may be met with in the meadows. Of course, grasses have their distinctive habitats the same as plants with more showy flowers, and some that grow on the moorlands and by mountain rills will not be found on cultivated ground; still, you will probably be astonished if you go through a meadow at this time and gather a single specimen of each of those that strike you as being different from those in your hand. Another thing that will strike you is the exceeding beauty and gracefulness of the individual grass stem, though its colouring runs only from green through yellow to white, with here and there perchance a touch of purple. But photographing them in the meadow is almost

27

out of the question. They are so much mixed up that it
is almost impossible to get a specimen sufficiently isolated
to show its character; and then, you might come twenty
times without finding the air sufficiently still to allow of
a photograph.

What with the Buttercups and the Ox-eye Daisies, one
might say on looking at the meadow from a distance that
there was no grass in it. Yellow and white almost hide the
green; but, of course, now we are in it we see that grass is
the basis of the whole thing. The path is almost hidden by
the encroachment of the exuberant vegetation from either
side.

See, on the margin of the field, Jack-by-the-Hedge is
still one of the most noticeable plants—still erect as ever.
Though he has been out so long we have not yet got a
suitable individual to stand for his portrait, and now as a
flower he is getting *passé*, for the earlier blossoms have
turned into long slender green pods, all standing erectly in
keeping with the general character of the plant. Oh! but
here are a few younger plants which have not got so far in
their development. Let us take advantage of the fact.
Whilst the portrait is being taken, amuse yourself by looking
over those older plants and see what you can find in the way
of caterpillars.

You remember that several times during our rambles we
have seen the dainty little Orange-tip Butterfly hovering
about these plants, and we have remarked that she would
be laying her eggs on them. Well, last month, had you
looked, you might have found just one orange egg on a
plant. If, perchance, you should find two caterpillars on
one plant you may be almost sure that each had a different
mother, for the Orange-tip does not lay her eggs in batches,
leaving the resulting caterpillars to distribute themselves:
she lays just one egg on a plant, so that the caterpillar has
no competition to meet, but has a little kingdom all to himself. He climbs up the flower-stem and finds that a seed-

Meadowsweet.

Hemlock-Leaved Water Dropwort.

pod is formed; very small it is, much about the same size, shape, and colour as himself. He is grey-green with a fine whitish line along each side, and the seed-pod has a similar line, so you may have a difficulty in telling one from the other. He is a very discerning caterpillar; in truth, you may feel inclined to credit him with penetrative vision, for he knows the exact location of a seed in the pod, and bites through the shell just above it. He eats the pod ultimately, but prefers to pick out the seeds first, just as a boy who intends to demolish a cake will start by picking out the plums.

And now let us get along to the waterside, and enjoy the fragrance of the Meadow-sweet (*Spiræa ulmaria*), whose plumy masses of white flowers are the most striking feature of the river banks just now. Here the plant restricts itself to the waterside, but we have seen many wet meadows full of it, and sometimes at considerable distance from a stream. You will probably be surprised to learn that the Meadow-sweet belongs to the Rose family. At first sight—looking at the flowers in the mass—you would be inclined to guess it had closer affinity to the Umbelliferous tribe; but, if you glance at the individual flowers of which the plumes are made up, you will no longer have doubts. And if you look at the fine leaves you will be reminded forcibly of the leaves of Agrimony and Silverweed, which are fashioned on similar lines though on a smaller scale. It is the interruptedly pinnate type of leaf again, and, somewhat like that of Silverweed, the underside is white and downy. The Meadow-sweet is one of those deceptive flowers that appear by their powerful fragrance to be attracting insects from far and near to come and drink deeply of abundant stores of nectar. But when they come there is never a drop of anything stronger than the dew that may have got caught in the tiny cups. But Rose-like it bears a crowd of stamens, and these produce much pollen—far more than is needed for fertilisation purposes, so the bees, beetles, and flies that can make use of that commodity are rewarded for their visits. And just look at some of those beetles that visit the flower. Brilliant *Donacias* who have just entered upon the enjoyment of sunshine after spending their grub stage among the roots of reeds and sedges in the muddy banks under water. They are slender beetles clad in green and copper-coloured mail, that glistens brightly in the sunshine as they fly and run over the flowers and herbage.

The Forget-Me-Not Gatherer.

It need not be said that the Meadow-sweet does not provide pollen for these creatures from purely philanthropic motives. Not at all. It wants the pollen interchanged between plant and plant. The pollen of one flower is all shed before the stigmas of that flower are fit to receive it; so, of necessity, every Meadow-sweet seed owes its existence to pollen brought from a younger flower.

Although Meadow-sweet is the most prominent in riverside vegetation to-day, there are other things, some of them,

Sulphur-Wort Water Dropwort.

from the colour of the flowers, liable to be lost sight of except as more Meadow-sweet. Here, for instance, where the river taking a wide curve has left considerable margin of swampy ground, there is a fine Umbelliferous plant, four or five feet in height, with stout hollow stems, and much divided, broad, wedge-shaped leaves. The white flowers are rather large for Umbellifers, and the umbels are again grouped in compound umbels. It is only just coming into flower, for most are in the bud stage. It is the Hemlock-leaved Water Dropwort (*Œnanthe crocata*)—one of the most virulently poisonous plants we have, and many cases are on record of death being caused by ignorant persons eating its thick root in mistake for Celery. Cattle and horses some-times make a similar mistake and pay the penalty with their lives.

Here is another member of the same genus—the Sulphur-wort Water Dropwort (*Œnanthe silaifolia*)—of much more slender proportions, but constructed on similar lines. Its leaves, however, instead of being broad, and intricately cut up, look more like stalks, and the umbels are smaller and fewer. It is a very pretty and graceful plant, two or three feet high.

There are Water-lily buds showing among the glossy leaves that float on the surface. On the opposite side of the river you can see the flowers of Buckbean. Close to the edge of the water there is a brilliant blue band of Forget-me-nots (*Myosotis palustris*)—with which a little maid is filling her basket—and above them are tall growths of Flag, and Bur-reed (*Sparganium ramosum*), with here and there what looks like Flowering Rush (*Butomus umbellatus*), but on neither of these two plants have the flowers yet appeared. Arrow-head (*Sagittaria sagittifolia*) and Water Plantain (*Alisma plantago*) send their leaves up from the water, and there is promise all around of a fine floral display here during the next month or so.

But it is time we were leaving the river to-day, for it

has turned westward, and will soon be losing itself in the dense shadows below the tree-clad hills.   Perhaps, however, there is more likelihood of our being lost, in a sense, in those wooded shades, for we should certainly find that they have their own floral attractions, which, in our case, must be reserved for another day.   So we will cross by this foot-bridge, and so avoid all risk of spoiling the sport of the two patient anglers under the Alder a little further along the stream.

"Losing itself below the Tree-Clad Hills."

Perfoliate Honeysuckle.

Among the Oaks

JULY IN THE WOOD.

WE will turn off the dusty highroad by the old church, which those learned in archæological matters tell us is Early English. It is certainly a picturesque structure, with its square tower surmounted by the shingle spire; but a good deal of its attractiveness is due to the fact that it is backed by the wood, whose bright foliage seems a very appropriate setting. There is a footpath just outside the low churchyard wall on either side, and both of them lead direct into the wood. They are not much used, as you may judge by the way the low branches of Beech and Whitebeam extend across and almost block them up. But you will find the obstruction yields to slight pressure, and, as you pass, the branches close like a door behind you and shut you in to all the beauties of this unfrequented spot.

Honeysuckle that has climbed as far as it could up the bushes has thrown out long new shoots with many a curve, and ending in clusters of the strong sweet-scented flowers that sway in the light breeze. And, mark you, this is not all common Honeysuckle (*Lonicera periclymenum*), but among it are plants of the Perfoliate Honeysuckle (*Lonicera caprifolium*), which is not supposed to occur wild in this part of the country. It is a plant introduced from the Continent in ancient times, and naturalised at Oxford and Cambridge, and we believe occurring in some other parts of the Eastern Counties. How it got into this wood it is impossible to say; but here it is quite wild. Its flowers are somewhat smaller, and proportionately more slender than those of the common kind, and it has broader leaves. But the distinctive feature consists in the fact that the upper pairs of leaves just below the flowers are half round, and their lower edges are completely united, so that the stem seems to pierce through a circular leaf. The cluster of flowers springs from the uppermost of these *connate* leaves without the intervention of a flower-stalk, as you see is the case in the common species. Another point of distinction is that the long corolla is split into four or five lobes instead of two parts. We must try to photograph this, though there is so much movement of the slender branches that we shall not be able to give it the full exposure it ought to have.

See what an extensive crop of Woodruff (*Asperula odorata*) is here under the Beeches, and much of it is still in flower; but probably these natural beds of Wild Strawberry (*Fragaria vesca*) will interest you more, for the fruit is now both ripe and abundant. There is also much Sanicle, and close by is the Field Scorpion-grass (*Myosotis arvensis*) whose names give too limited an idea of the places where it grows. It is certainly found as much in open spaces in the wood and copse as in fields; but there is a distinct Wood Scorpion-grass (*Myosotis sylvatica*), of much less frequent occurrence, and this fact no doubt led to our present species being dubbed *arvensis*. It is to be regretted that the scientific sponsors of plants did not give more descriptive names whilst they were about it. Many of such names are

Field Scorpion-Grass.

quite beyond cavil; but there are many that leave much to
be desired in this respect. However, our plant *is Myosotis
arvensis,* and such we must be content to call it, even
though we have found it growing profusely in this wood.
You will observe that it differs greatly from the Forget-me-
not (*Myosotis palustris*) which we found by the waterside,
first, in its more scanty foliage and generally attenuated
appearance; its leaves and stems are hairy, whereas the other
was smooth in all its parts, and these flowers are about
one-third smaller than the others. At the same time there
is so strong a family likeness that you felt justified in saying
the moment you saw it—this is one of the Forget-me-nots.

You ask why there should be this difference in respect
of the hairy covering of the plant? It is now a generally
accepted truth, verified by observations on many plants, that
these short hairs have been developed as a hindrance to
troublesome little insects that are fond of climbing to the
flowers and helping themselves to pollen and honey without
being able to render any services in return. It is almost
certain that such growths are not induced by the plants'
desire to furnish botanists with the means of separating
allied species—as some writers of a past generation appeared
to imagine. In the woods and fields there are multitudes
of such small creeping insects; but plants that grow with
their roots in the water are free from this annoyance. And
so, though you will find innumerable land plants with such
protective hairs, you will also notice their entire absence in
the case of aquatic plants. The Forget-me-not is an example:
its stems and leaves are smooth, and the few scattered hairs
upon it are not sufficiently numerous to act as a deterrent.
A similar contrast is afforded by the Speedwells: the land
species are all hairy, but the Brooklime, which grows with
its lower parts in water, is polished.

One other point about the Scorpion-grasses is worth
mentioning now that we have one of them before us, though
the special point will not arise until the flowers have been

succeeded by seeds. These plants do not produce a general pod or capsule in which the seeds are contained, but each seed has its own separate shell scarcely larger than itself—they are in fact nutlets, like those of the Strawberry and the Buttercups, though of different shape. These, when ripe, lie loosely in the closed calyx, which thus becomes a substitute for a capsule. Now, in all our four land species of *Myosotis* the calyx is covered with hooked hairs which catch in the fur or feathers of animals—or in your clothes for the matter of that—and get carried away, dropping out the polished nutlets as they go. Such an arrangement would be useless by the stream, for it would probably result in many seeds being scattered far from the water. The stream is the best agent for their dispersal in the case of the aquatic species; and so we find that the calyces of both our aquatics are without these hooked hairs. Does not that look like evidence?

We have been considering one of the smaller beauties of the wood; now look before you at those imposing masses of rosy purple, some of the plants as tall as yourself. Look down that glade, whose far end appears to be blocked by tens of thousands of the same plant. The artist who delights in a broad splash of fine colour on his canvas could get it here; and when you have satisfied your colour-sense with gazing on the distant mass, we will pay more particular attention to the individual plants of which it is composed. Our gardens can scarcely show anything finer than that; but unfortunately this plant is far too vigorous to be tolerated in any well-ordered garden—it would want to take entire possession. "What is it?" Oh, we forgot to mention its name. It is one of the Willow Herbs, commonly known as the Rose-bay or French Willow (*Epilobium angustifolium*).

Willow-herb is a name easy to understand. The leaves are of much the same shape as those of the Willow, though it is perhaps unnecessary to state that there is no relationship between the two. To some persons the leaves may have suggested those of the Bay-tree, and the prefix Rose signified the Bay with rosy flowers. We fear that the other prefix— French—was given in anything but the complimentary sense in which, in these *l'entente cordiale* days, we should apply it now, and that it must be classed with those terms of belittlement—such as Dog Mercury and Cow Parsnip—to which we have already referred. But no matter what may have been in the minds of our ancestors when they bestowed these names, and by whichever one we prefer to know the plant to-day, we must admit its great beauty. Though we may decide to refuse it admittance to our gardens we should be very sorry to have it banished from the woods, of which it is one of the freshest and brightest of ornaments.

There are two or three points we should take note of before we get away from a close inspection of the Willow-herb. First of all, it has probably struck you that these flowers differ from the majority of plants we have met with, in the fact that they have but four petals, and that the limb of the calyx has only four lobes, to correspond. Count the stamens and you will see further correspondence—they are twice four, one to each sepal and each petal. The ovary has four cells, and the thread-like style divides at the tip into four stigmas. The flowers are, therefore, very uniform in all their parts. Another point to make note of is, that the ovary is very long, and below the flower. Ah! that you had not noticed, and thought the ovary was part of the flower-stalk. In these points the Willow Herb's flowers agree with the Evening Primrose of your garden, and therefore you will not be surprised to learn that both plants belong to one family.

One of our native shrubs that gets frequently passed by without recognition during the greater part of the year, now forces itself upon our attention by means of its creamy-white flowers. The shrub is the Dogwood or Cornel (*Cornus sanguinea*). It is frequently confused with the Privet (*Ligustrum vulgare*), but there is really no excuse for this error, for though both grow to seven or eight feet and have more or less oval leaves, these differ greatly in texture; for whilst those of the Privet are stiff and glossy and borne erectly, those of the Dogwood are rather soft, strongly nerved, and droop from the stems. In winter, whilst the Privet is still partially clothed, the Dogwood loses every leaf, and its bark turns red, as its leaves did before they fell. Both bear clusters of small white flowers, but whereas those of Privet are in tapering panicles, those of Dogwood are in flatter cymes. These are very small—only about one-third of an inch across—but their smallness is compensated by their grouping, and by the great number of the clusters, which are well distributed over the upper shoots. Such a display as we have now before us makes the bush very noticeable, so that there is no reason why the plant should not be well-known. In the days when wood was widely used for small purposes for which metal is now substituted, the Dogwood must have been very familiar, and its numerous names testify to this fact.

The name Dogwood is not in the same category as Dog's Mercury, Dog Daisy, and the like, though the old herbalists who had lost the original significance of the name imputed to it virtues in the cure of mangy dogs. It is properly Dag-wood, *i.e.*, wood proper for making into dags or skewers, for which its toughness made it specially suitable; and its scientific name *Cornus* has similar reference to its *horniness*. The flowers are succeeded in autumn by small berries of a black hue. Note that the floral parts are in fours—four teeth to the calyx, four petals to the corolla, four stamens. The Dogwood has only one British relation—the Dwarf Cornel (*Cornus suecica*), which is a small herb, only a few inches high, restricted to the alpine moors of Yorkshire and the more northern parts of our island.

Last month we found the Common Mallow (*Malva sylvestris*), and we have come upon it frequently since. Now we have met with another member of the same genus, for

Rose-Bay Willow-Herb.

this group of tall plants before us with delicate rose-pink flowers and finely divided leaves is the Musk Mallow (*Malva moschatus*). The Common Mallow is a fine plant when growing away from the dusty roads, where it is most frequently seen; but though from the colour point of view the Musk Mallow is perhaps not so striking, it is in our opinion the more beautiful of the two. It is no more strictly a woodland plant than the Common Mallow which is called *sylvestris*, for it grows in meadows; but we have mostly found the finest specimens on the borders of the wood, in woodland clearings or in thin copses. It is a hairy plant, and its stems are sometimes spotted with purple. The long-stalked leaves are broken up into five or seven slender lobes, and these are again cut up pinnately into smaller divisions in a way that suggests some affinity with the Scented Geranium of our conservatories. The flowers produce honey, and the arrangement of their organs is similar to what is found in the Common Mallow.

Small Heath Butterfly.

Do you see that old head on one of last year's Knapweeds that has strangely survived the storms of winter and spring? Do you see what is on it? It is the Small Heath Butterfly (*Cœnonympha pamphilus*) at rest—probably one of the second brood newly emerged from the chrysalis, and so hanging to give its wings time to harden before trying their powers. We will not disturb it, but take advantage of its stillness to get its portrait. It is one of our most plentiful species, the most constant companion of our summer rambles, across fields and commons especially. In the caterpillar state it feeds on grasses, and, judging from the prevalence of the butterfly, the larvæ must consume a good deal, but one never hears of the destruction caused by it. It is probably a case of "what the eye don't see the heart won't grieve about." The depredation of the caterpillars of the White Butterflies (*Pieris brassicæ* and *P. rapæ*) is only too evident in our cabbage patch, and as cabbage is a food of man we grieve accordingly; but as the ravages of the Small Heath Caterpillar are largely unseen, and grass is not directly human food, we do not grudge the handful or so of fodder that each consumes.

At every few steps we take now, along the grassy glades, we come upon the bright cymes of pink-flowered Centaury (*Erythræa centaurium*), that is abundant also in the pastures. All the Gentian family have singularly neat and pretty flowers, and the Centaury is no exception. Here they are funnel-shaped, the broad open portion being divided into four or five lobes. There is much about the plant that reminds one of its not distant relative the Yellow-wort (*Blackstonia perfoliata*) that we found on the Downs the other day. The radical leaves are oval, but they get narrower as we proceed up the stem; and they are in pairs whose bases are connected, as we found in Yellow-wort. Like Yellow-wort, too, the corolla does not fall off when the flower has been fertilised, but remains to wrap up the swelling seed-capsule. It is a very variable plant, and consequently the "splitters" have been at work on it, and have made six or seven doubtful species out of it.

Do you notice how thickly the ground under the trees is covered with young Oaks? They are the produce of last year's acorns, which, after lying all through the winter among the dead leaves, germinated in May, afterwards sending up thin spindly shoots that would grow into fair saplings and ultimately into veterans of the forest such as you see around.

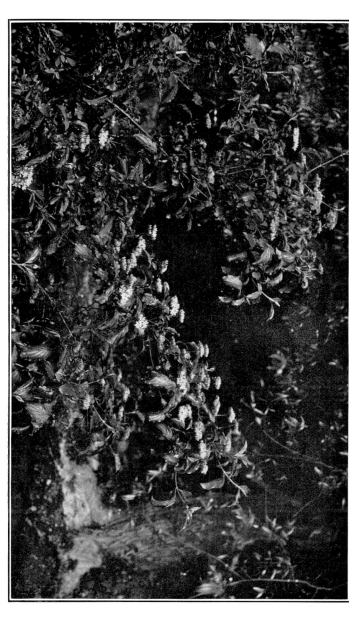

Dogwood.

But not one in a hundred of all these crowded seedlings will ever attain to the proportions of a small tree. Innumerable enemies are lying in wait for them now, and as soon as they have developed sufficiently to be worth attention caterpillars will destroy their leaves and sap their vitality, just as they

Stag-Beetles.

try to do with the giants of the race. Then there are the rabbits that will browse them level with the earth. The old Oaks are pretty full of insect life just now. Caterpillars swarm upon the leaves, some having secured privacy by rolling the edge of a leaf over and securing it by silken

II.—G

filaments so that they can lie snugly and feed at pleasure; others apparently lose foothold easily, for they hang suspended by invisible silken ropes and dangle in our faces as we pass beneath. Stag-beetles (*Lucanus cervus*), the giants of their tribe, so far at least as these islands are concerned, pass their days among the foliage and at evening may be seen flying round the trees. But the Oaks have interest for other creatures besides insects. Here, artfully concealed in a little hollow beneath the starting off of a big branch, a Wren has made her mossy nest, with a good handful of dried bracken to serve as a foundation. How she managed to fix her nest in such a place is a subject for wonder, for there are no projecting shoots beneath it.

Many of these trees have smoothly-chiselled round holes in the bark, testifying to the industry of the Woodpeckers who have probably been seeking for the fat grubs of the Stag-beetles, which spend their ante-beetle days feeding in the timber. Many of the holes eaten by decay into the stouter trunks are the homes of Owls of several species; and here is evidence that this tree is made use of by another bird. These empty nutshells, wedged into the crevices of the bark, were placed there as whole nuts by the Nuthatch (*Sitta cæsia*), and hammered with her beak until the shell broke and yielded up the juicy kernel. Almost every one of the old Oaks bears a number of these broken shells fixed in the bark. The Squirrel in Emerson's fable considered the chief purpose of the mountain was to make "a very pretty Squirrel-track," and probably the Nuthatch considers the rough Oak-bark a special arrangement to simplify the cracking of nuts for her. But it should be said that the bird fully repays the Oak for this convenience, for all through the summer she is busy—that is her "twee, twee, twee," sounding above us now—destroying multitudes of the Oak's insect enemies. It is only in autumn and winter, when insect life is scarce, that she ekes out such supplies by adding hazel-nuts and beech-mast to her bill of fare.

Musk Mallow.

Another of the St. John's Worts is out in flower. This one, growing in tall clumps beside our path, is the Perforated St. John's Wort (*Hypericum perforatum*), one of the three commonest species. It is a beautiful plant, always looking fresh and neat, even after it has endured all the heats of summer, and its leaves have turned red and its petals have wound themselves round the resinous capsule. Note the regularity with which the narrow stalkless leaves are given off in pairs, and how symmetrically the many branches are arranged, also in pairs. The leaves, if you hold them up to the light, appear to be perforated as with a pin; but this is but an illusion, though it appears to have imposed upon the early bestowers of plant names. Even Linneus called it *perforatum*, but it must be presumed that he did so out of respect for the

How the Nuthatch cracks her Nuts.

folk-name, for he must have seen, as you see, that the so-called perforations are really pellucid glands without colouring matter. The St. John's Worts are "great on glands," and some of them have them raised above the surface and of a black hue. In this specimen the veins of the leaves also are pellucid. The flowers in this species are much more numerous than in the Tutsan, and the proportions between leaf and flower are reversed. There we had leaves four or five times larger than the flowers; here the bright yellow flowers are quite twice the size of the leaves. This is the plant that was—and still is in some places—held to be such a valuable ally in warding off the machinations of witches, warlocks, and all other evil powers. One of its old names was *Fuga demonum,* but in order to avail oneself fully of its virtues it had to be gathered on St. John's Eve. A bunch of St. John's Wort hung over the door would prevent the entry of evil powers; and it was one of the "sovraine herbes" of the rustic pharmacopœia.

It seems but a little while since we noted with pleasure the first appearance of the hook-like frond-buds of Bracken-fern (*Pteris aquilina*) coming through the earth whilst the Blue-bells were abundant. Now the Bracken has reached its full development, and many of the fronds in this wood are quite as tall as we are, and of breadth exceeding ours. As the light comes through their tissues we see how great a difference in appearance is effected by a change of habitat. Out on the open heaths the Bracken is an opaque, coarse-textured plant of half the height. Here it looks as tender as a Lady-fern, and every minute division of the frond is flatly spread, instead of the whole frond being curled up as it is in the open. We regard it as too coarse a plant for cultivation, but the woodland examples show us that coarseness or delicacy is in this case a question of environment. The truth is, the Bracken is not the rough hardy plant that it is commonly supposed to be. At the end of May, in the present year, we saw the Bracken over a large stretch of Surrey common, partially sheltered by woods, standing all brown and withered as though fire had passed over it, but these effects were solely due to the cold winds and frosts of the later half of "the merry month."

The fact of its natural tenderness should be obvious from a consideration of its habits. Nearly all our ferns manifest their hardiness by forming crowns above the surface of the soil, relying for protection from frosts upon the coat of chaffy scales with which their frond-buds are covered.

Perforated St. John's Wort.

II. *Pl.* 23.   *G* 45.

Bracken.

The Bracken, in common with the Marsh - fern (*Lastrea thelypteris*), the Moonwort (*Botrychium lunaria*), and Adder's-tongue (*Ophioglossum vulgatum*), keeps underground in winter. Instead of forming a tufted, erect rootstock, the Bracken root-stock is horizontal and of considerable length, the fronds rising from it at distant intervals, and having to push their way up through a foot or more—sometimes many feet—of soil to the surface. This fact is sufficient to account for the unexpanded frond being hooked at its extremity rather than coiled in a flat spiral, the former shape being more suited for piercing the earth.

The Bracken is now coming into fruit, and if you turn over the frond, so as to show the underside, you will see that the margins of the ultimate divisions of the frond are folded over to cover the continuous lines of spore-cases. The spores themselves are not ripe yet; when they are, the cases will burst and the spores will lie like a fine dusty rust along the margins. The way to properly appreciate the abundance of the spores is to walk through a fern-brake in August or September, and when you emerge your clothing will have turned to a rusty hue.

Many of the open spaces at this upper end of the wood are now filled with continuous growths of Ragwort (*Senecio jacobœa*), a very near relation of the common Groundsel (*Senecio vulgaris*) that becomes a nuisance in the garden. Yet how unlike the Ragwort is to that rather squalid and poverty-stricken annual, that appears to hang its flower-heads in shame for having come down in the world. For we may be certain, when we consider the other *Senecios*, that the Groundsel has seen better days. Once it may have had conspicuous heads of flowers with bright yellow ray-florets like those of Ragwort; but now it seldom has a ray. The Ragwort, on the contrary, is a fine perennial, with a stout leafy stem, three or four feet in height, and the leaves large and boldly lobed. The flower-heads are about an inch across, but they are made far more conspicuous by

being massed in dense corymbs terminating the stems.
And then you get it growing in such enormous communities
that it will occupy many contiguous acres of ground, providing a continuous sheet of golden colour.

The Ragwort would not be tolerated in fields that are
at all well looked after; but out in the woods, and on any
expanse of waste or neglected land, it has things much its
own way, in spite of the fact that Nature has told off a
special policeman to keep it somewhat in check. The
policeman in this case takes the form of a handsome caterpillar, which you may find in scores on almost every
Ragwort plant. The rings of which the bodies of caterpillars are always built up are here alternately orange and
black—a conjunction which insect-eating birds understand
to signify that the wearer of that livery is of a nauseous
flavour and better left alone. So you see them here feeding
in the most open way in broad daylight, not hiding under
the leaves, but stretched along the stems, or on the surface
of the leaves, and even among the flowers. In most of these
situations the caterpillar of the Cinnabar Moth (*Euchelia
jacobϾ*) is very conspicuous, but it has also a favourite
trick of curling itself round the stems, when it becomes
a flower to all appearance. When the Ragwort flower is
fading after fertilisation, the yellow rays curve downwards;
and this appearance the Cinnabar caterpillar's orange rings
exactly simulate, whilst the black rings supply the deep
shadow that appears under the flower in strong sunlight.
This is rather a remarkable circumstance in connection with
an insect protected by warning colours; but it may be that
some of its enemies are too ignorant to understand the
meaning of such colours, and might inflict damage before
they discovered their mistake. But it is difficult to
harmonise the caution implied in this mimicry of the fading
flower with the boldness with which they expose themselves
on other parts of the plant.

There are several Cinnabar Moths flitting about the

Ragwort.

Ragwort, their fore-wings of a dingy black or olive-brown, on which are laid two marginal bars of crimson extending to nearly the length of the wing; also two roundish spots of the same colour. The hinder-wings have this colouring pretty well reversed, for the ground is crimson margined with black.

Away from what we call the Ragwort field, and into the shade of the trees again, we come upon a number of plants with long slender racemes of pale pink flowers. The plant is about a couple of feet in height, and quite half of that length consists of the raceme. The oval opposite leaves are on long stalks, and are faintly toothed. Their general appearance reminds one strongly of the Deadly Nightshade (*Atropa belladonna*) on a small scale, and there can be little doubt that this resemblance struck our own ancestors, for the plant is named Enchanter's Nightshade (*Circœa lutetiana*). Seeing that Circe is commemorated in the scientific name, the English ought to be Enchantress' Nightshade; but the plant is not known to have been used in magical preparations, so the names may be only poetical references to the places where it grows as suitable resorts for that mythical class of person. In the woods of the northern hills there is another and smaller species, the Alpine Enchanter's Nightshade (*Circœa alpina*), with each petal almost divided into two petals. On examining the flowers you will probably be surprised to find that it has only two petals. The lobes of the calyx are two to correspond, there are only two stamens, and the thread-like style ends in a two-lobed stigma. You will remember that the Rose-bay Willow-herb had four petals, and other parts to correspond, and that we mentioned it was a member of the same family as the Evening Primrose. Enchanter's Nightshade is also a member of the same family, and it is probable that this represents the more primitive type of flower in the family. The flower-parts are in agreement with the paired leaves, from which the flower-parts are considered to have been evolved.

Ah, we know that whistle. It is the keeper going his round with a wooden basket of pheasant food upon his arm. The young Pheasants are now at large in the woods, though their foster-mothers are shut up in coops, between whose bars the chicks can pass freely, that they may return to the shelter of the hen's wings in case of danger. They know the keeper's whistle, too; and though a minute or two ago they were invisible, among the ferns and other undergrowth, they now come running from all sides and tumbling over one another in their haste to share the food

The Keeper and his Pheasant Chicks.

he is scattering. He is properly proud of his young birds, and suggests that we should " get a snap at them " whilst he feeds them. We try it, but whilst the grain is on the ground not a head is still enough to make an impression on the plate, though their bodies will come all right. Still

Bramble.

there is the keeper quiet enough, and with his charming
surroundings he is sufficient for a picture. All through the
wood he goes whistling, wherever he has got a coop laid,
and near each coop, four times a day, he scatters his mixture
of grain and meal and minced meat. Thousands of children

"Ferns beside the Way."

are less carefully fed than are these birds, and the pity is
that these beautiful creatures are so carefully tended only
that they may be slaughtered at the fall of the year.

As we pass out of the wood by one of these green alleys
we are charmed by the beauty of the ferns that grow beside

II.—H

our way, every frond exhibiting grace of form and disposition, and all as orderly as though some clever landscape gardener had arranged them; but for pleasing, unstudied effects of this kind Nature is the best landscape gardener.

Go quietly now. That is a Mole just ahead. He has come up for a breath of fresh air and has evidently strayed away from his runs, for the ground outside the wood has been baked hard by the July sun and he finds it difficult to dig into it. See how he labours with his spade-like hands. Ah! he has got a softer spot now, and the mould flies behind him. Nose and hands are at work, and having pierced the harder upper crust he makes rapid headway. There goes his funny little tail—exit *Talpa europœa*. He is about the quaintest figure among the small number of British beasts. He is a nuisance when he gets into the garden and travels under the well-kept lawn, but it is to be hoped that the Mole-trapper will not succeed in entirely extirpating him, for he does much good, in spite of the agricultural opinions to the contrary.

The Mole.

Fly Agaric.

The Road across the Heath.

JULY ON THE HEATH.

WE have given a long rest to the sandy tracts with their high pine-woods and their broad expanses of Gorse and Heather. They are really always interesting, but now their grand season has opened, and for at least three months the heath-lands will be a blaze of rich colour. It is time we revelled in their glories. We shall not have much company, for at this time of the year ramblers prefer to keep in the shade of the woods, alleging that the heath is too hot and too exposed. But, should you find it so, we can promise you that there are many hollows where one can sit for a rest on the clean soft sand in the shade of tall Furze and Broom and Bracken. Even the Purple Heath and the Heather are tall enough in places to give shade to such a hollow, and there are clumps of graceful Birches standing like oases in the desert.

Among the first of the heath plants to attract our attention—though, as you are well aware, it is in no sense confined

51

to or more abundant on heaths—is the Bramble (*Rubus fruticosus*). It is now in flower, and we shall be meeting with it everywhere in field, wood, lane, and common; but we must pay attention to it somewhere, and as this bush has some of the finest flowers we have seen this season, let us photograph it. Yes, I know what you are going to say: that these flowers are much larger and whiter than usual. The Bramble is one of the most variable plants we have, and there are botanists who have become Bramble specialists and are trying to mark down all these variations and give them distinctive names. Only, these gentlemen instead of calling them varieties regard each variation as a separate species, so that if you consult the *London Catalogue of British Plants* you will find the genus Rubus represented by a complete century of species, whilst if you consult Hooker's *Students' Flora* you will find four species only, with twenty-two sub-species and a prodigious number of varieties set down under *Rubus fruticosus*. Now, we want to get some speaking acquaintance with our native flora in general, and as botany is not the sole business of our lives we have not time to consider the Bramble in a state of minute sub-division, so we will be content with calling this specimen *Rubus fruticosus*. Between ourselves, we believe the specialists call this *Rubus thyrsoideus*, but you never can be sure unless you have the specialists' own named specimens before you for reference.

By far the larger number of Bramble-bushes around us are covered with small pink flowers—Tennyson's

"Bramble-roses faint and pale"

—but trailing close to the ground there is another form that even most people who are not Bramble-specialists can distinguish by its different habit, its white woolly sepals and its more glaucous foliage. This is the Dewberry (*var. cæsius*), that is the first to ripen its fruit, which has fewer but much larger globular drupes. These we shall find fit to eat in about a month from now, when the ordinary Blackberries will be still green and red.

Although the Bramble flowers are so like those of the Wild Roses, the fruit is as unlike as it well could be; but the Rose-family though exhibiting such uniformity in its flowers is very diverse, so far as its fruits are concerned. And yet, if we look closely into these fruits, we shall find a larger amount of agreement than appears on a superficial view. The Brambles come closer to the Plum and Cherry section of the family than to the Wild Roses and Apples. If we regard each of the globules on a Blackberry separately we shall find that its structure is very similar to that of a Plum or a Cherry. The "stone" of the larger fruit is represented by the "pip" of the Blackberry.

The recent heavy rains, which we get almost invariably about the middle of July, have refreshed the heath wonderfully, and we shall be surprised, when we reach this clump of Birches, if we do not find that it has started the first of the autumnal toadstools. It is early to talk of autumn, it is true, but there is an imperceptible gliding of one season into another. Many of the autumnal flowers first make their appearance in summer, and so it is also with the fungi which are so strong a characteristic of autumn. Here they are. Several well expanded, and many others in various stages of development. This is known as the Fly Agaric (*Amanita muscarius*). Most persons know this by sight, because its bright red cap, flecked with little bits of creamy-white kid apparently, attracts attention at once. If you glance at these specimens that are just emerging through the soil you will understand what these flecks are. In an early underground stage these fungi were invested with an outer skin, of similar texture to the inner skin between the peel and flesh of an orange. The mushroom expands rapidly by filling its myriad cells with water, but the wrapper does not grow, so it gets split up into small fragments. These newly appeared, almost globular, heads are entirely clad in

it, except those that have had to push their way through
grass roots which have more or less cleaned it off. Others
show several splits in the white wrapper, through which the
red shows in strong contrast. The one we are about to
photograph has so far expanded that these particles are
distant from each other and arranged in concentric rings.
Below the cap we find radiating plates set edgewise, much as
we found them in St. George's Mushroom, and as you would
find them in the Common Mushroom that you get from the
greengrocer, that is if you are so fortunate as to get them in
an unbroken and fresh condition. These plates, or "gills,"
support the microscopic spores, which are produced in
millions, and by which the species is reproduced.

The Fly Agaric is one of our indubitably poisonous
mushrooms. The popular notion is, that any kind of mushroom that is not sold by the greengrocer is either poisonous
or at least open to grave suspicion of being so, and therefore
must not be called mushroom but toadstool. The truth is,
that of the enormous number of species found in these
islands there is only a small percentage of which we know
beyond question whether they are wholesome or noxious
when used as food. On the other hand, a considerable
number of those eaten experimentally are known without
doubt to be wholesome, and of these some are known to be
even superior to the mushroom of commerce—even though
they have only grown among leaf-mould instead of on a
manure-heap!

Take, for example, this other kind that grows in the same
Birch-clump, and which you might be forgiven for supposing is of the same species but of another colour. Its
cap is brown, and the flecks of skin are brownish-grey, but
the stem and gills, which remain creamy-white in the Fly
Agaric, in this species have a reddish tinge, and wherever it
may be touched it turns a rusty red. This sensitiveness to
touch and the manifestation of red has caused one author to
term it the Blusher (*Amanita rubescens*), and as it had no

Blusher Agaric.

English name given to it by our ancestors that name may as well stand. What we started to say, however, when we were led into a description, was this: the Blusher is appreciated by those who know it as far superior to the Common Mushroom (*Agaricus campestris*). But then there are those flecks upon its cap, so like to the known poisonous Fly Agaric—for that was formerly used to poison fly-papers,

Brimstone Butterfly.

hence the name; and the intelligent British citizen confesses his inability to remember the points of difference between them, and goes on paying a shilling or sixteenpence a pound for broken, maggoty mushrooms, when he might go to the woods and commons and have the pleasure of selecting the choicest specimens for nothing.

We were about to call your attention to the fact that the Heaths (*Erica*) are out, but first let us take the opportunity of photographing this Brimstone Butterfly (*Gonepteryx rhamni*) that is patiently waiting on a Heath-bell among these seedling Birches. He is by no means a characteristic butterfly of July, and we met many of his kind in our spring rambles, but they were so pleased to welcome the sunshine after their long hibernation that they could not stay to give us a sitting. This one has but recently emerged from the chrysalis, and has been resting here to give its wings time to expand fully; but that process being completed we must quickly avail ourselves of the opportunity afforded, or the Brimstone will be off to test its powers of flight. This specimen is of a later generation than those we saw in spring. The eggs were laid on the Buckthorn at the beginning of May, and by the end of June the caterpillars resulting therefrom had entered the chrysalis stage, from which the perfect insect emerged about a fortnight later.

A purple tint is coming over all the heath, due to the opening of the flowers of Fine-leaved Heath (*Erica cinerea*) and Heather (*Calluna vulgaris*). In the hollows, where the ground is damper, there is another species, the Cross-leaved Heath (*Erica tetralix*), with fewer, but finer, flowers of a rosy-pink, paling to white on the undersides of its large pitcher-shaped flowers. Fine-leaved Heath everybody knows, though they do not always know it by name. In August all the tailors in the West End of London exhibit it in their windows as a reminder that the shooting season is approaching, and that now is the time to order appropriate costumes to go a-shooting in. But most of them imagine they are showing Scotch Heather! though there is nothing distinctively Scottish about Heather, for it grows, as you see, plentifully over the heaths and moors of Surrey. We have often been shown with pride a tuft of Heather "received this morning from Scotland," though the recipient, had he known it, might have gathered an exactly similar tuft within half a mile of his own residence. Heather grows north, east, south, and west in our islands,

Heather.

and is among the most generally distributed of our wild plants. For botanical purposes the United Kingdom is divided into one hundred and twelve counties, and Heather occurs naturally in one hundred and eleven of them.

Here, as we said, are Heather and two Heaths growing side by side, so that it is quite easy to compare them if you have any fear of labelling Heath as Heather. The Heather - flowers, you see, are quite minute and of a rosy - purple colour, which applies to both corolla and calyx. The striking thing in connection with the Heather-flower is that the calyx is much larger than the corolla. It consists of four separate sepals, and the corolla though in one piece is almost divided into four petals. Many

Caterpillar of Emperor Moth.

persons are imposed upon by this arrangement, and the imposition is helped by the slender green bracts at the base of the calyx, which look like real sepals. Both calyx and corolla are, like the Heaths, built of a thin parchmenty material, which does not wither when fertilisation has taken place, but retains much of its shape through the winter and

II.—I

spring. To detect its leaves one wants almost to use a lens, for they are so minute and overlap one another so closely that they look more like a scaly cuticle to the woody branches which they effectually clothe. Through the pocket-lens the leaves are seen to be in whorls of four, and this gives a four-angled appearance to the branches.

But your eyes are on that patch of Cross-leaved Heath in the hollow. Let us go to it. This, you see, though closely allied to the Heather has the flowers constructed differently. The sepals keep their proper place and do not attempt to pass themselves off as petals. The petals are entirely united to form an egg-shaped tube with a small mouth, which is neatly finished off with four turned-down lobes. These corollas, in addition to the difference of colour already noted, are rendered distinct from the Fine-leaved Heath by their being stouter, and also by the way they are borne. Those of the Fine-leaved Heath are in whorls at intervals up the stem : these are all gathered into a drooping umbel at the summit of the stem. Then the whole aspect of the plants is different. Fine-leaved Heath is altogether smooth and dark ; Cross-leaved Heath is downy all over and grey, the tips of the shoots almost white. If you will remember these few points, you need never fear mixing up the two common species, nor confuse either with the Heather.

Wait a moment! Do you see that beautiful caterpillar on that bit of Bramble growing among the Heather? He is coloured a beautiful green, and every one of the fat segments of which his body is built up bears a circle of pink warts from which clusters of hairs and bristles are given off. It is the caterpillar of the Emperor Moth (*Saturnia carpini*), and it feeds upon a variety of heath-plants besides Bramble. About the end of August he will spin a white silken cocoon among the Heather, in which he will contrive a clever doorway of short stiff hairs that keep tightly closed against intruders, but which will afford

Cross-Leaved Heath.

Harebell.

easy egress when, next April or May, he emerges as a beautiful moth.

The Harebell (*Campanula rotundifolia*) usually keeps time with the Heaths, and here, up to date, it springs alike from the short rabbit-cropped turf and from thick clumps of tall Heather.

There is a great difference in the stature of individual plants, some of them being only a few inches high, whilst here is one among the Heather that is nearly three feet. Of course the height of the Heather has necessitated its taller growth, but it is not in consequence weak and poor; on the contrary, the flowers are finer than the

Emperor Moth and Cocoon.

average specimens. Several of our native Bell-flowers are common, and we shall probably meet with one or two more in our rambles during the next two months; but the Harebell is certainly the most graceful and the most popular of them. Who that sees them hanging above the turf or Heather can refrain from gathering a few of the flowers?

The proper name of this plant, reflected in the scientific name, appears to be the Round-leaved Bell-flower, and this has long been a standing joke among those who know it only when in flower. Trace down the slender stem until you come to the leaves, and you will see that they are long and narrow. Why then should it be called *rotundifolia*? It never has round leaves, but the first ones put forth close to the ground are oval with a heart-shaped base, and this appears to have been near enough to round to satisfy the early botanists; but had they been absolutely round we feel that it was scarcely justifiable to take so temporary a character as a foundation for a name. Search right down to the root and you will find no such leaves now, because when the stem begins to lengthen these early leaves are absorbed. Linneus is usually credited with the perpetration of this scientific joke, and it is true that by adopting it he gave permanence to the name; but it had really been in use, by botanists in this country, at least two hundred years before the great Swede took in hand the reduction of the animal and vegetable chaos to some kind of order. The story is told how he found a young plant of Harebell with its "round" leaves growing at Upsala, and those who are aware that the questionable name was used by Gerarde in his *Herball* have discredited the story as apocryphal; but this need not be so. Such a discovery may have decided him upon retaining the old name. However, we need not quarrel with the name; it has the argument from ancient usage to recommend it, and those who object to it as misleading can stick to Harebell, which everybody understands to-day, though in early Victorian times there was confusion between *Campanula rotundifolia* and *Scilla nutans* when Harebell was mentioned.

You are quite right: it *is* time we got back to the flower and left the names. Throughout the Bell-flower family the five petals are united into a tube of some sort, and it mostly takes the bell-form. The sepals are similarly united into

Harebell.

Silverweed.

a tubular calyx having five free lobes like the corolla. There are five stamens, and the pistil when mature splits at its upper extremity into three or five arms, which are the stigmas. Now, look into this newly opened flower, and you will see the five stamens all standing close against the pistil, which at present ends in a thickened club-like portion. The style or lower portion is beset by hairs, though these are mostly hidden just now. The base of each stamen is very broad, and the reason for this is that the basal expansion covers a honey gland. In order to get at the honey a bee has to alight on the pistil, which stands in the centre like the clapper of a bell—to which the clubbed head gives it additional resemblance—and thrust his tongue down between the stamens. The anthers shed their pollen against the hairy portion of the style, to which it adheres, and then the upper portions of the stamens turn away from the style, and wither. Their work is done and they get out of the way.

Here is an older flower. See, here are the withered stamens, and around the style a thick muffler of pollen. The club has opened out and separated into three stigmas, which occupy a good deal of the mouth of the bell. An alighting bee clings to the stigmas, and if he has been in another flower his underside is coated with pollen, some of which adheres to these stigmas. That is the first stage. Next he puts himself right for the honey, and climbs up the style to reach it. In so doing he crawls over the muffler of pollen, and a good deal of it is carried away by his hairy underside. That is the second stage. Having got all the honey available he departs, and makes for another flower of the same kind—leaves some of his load of pollen on the stigmas and takes up a fresh supply. And so on, always effecting a cross between different flowers of the same species.

The authors of the Paley school used to explain the hanging of the Harebell flowers by the necessity for pro-

tecting the honey from deterioration by rain and dew, re-
gardless of the fact that there are numerous honey-producing
flowers that are erect and therefore open to this deterioration.
It seems more probable, in the light that we now have on
the matter, that it is to protect the honey from ants and
other honey-seekers who give no *quid pro quo*.   The exterior
of the bell is perfectly smooth, and such insects, after the
laborious climb up the hair-like foot-stalk, would have great
difficulty in maintaining their hold in descending to the
mouth of the bell, and clinging on whilst they doubled the
thin edge.   If they got so far another difficulty would meet
them, for the inner walls are protected by barriers of hairs
which prevent access to the honey that way.   Another day
we hope to show you conclusively that the Harebell does not
hang down for the purpose of keeping out rain or dew.

There is an interesting corner of the Heath with a bit
of boggy ground which would repay a visit just now, but
we have not time to-day, and must reserve it for an early
ramble when we can strike across to the river and make
acquaintance with some charming waterside plants.   For the
present we will take this lane back, and we are sure to find
some things of interest on our way.

Here, for example, by the roadside are crowds of plants,
but nearest to us is one of the prettiest leaves our weeds offer
us.   It is our old friend the interruptedly-pinnate leaf, but
this time it belongs to Silverweed (*Potentilla anserina*), and
the plant is in flower too.   Buttercups, many people would
say, but they are Golden Roses again.   The leaves are much
after the fashion of Agrimony, though not so large ; but these
are more beautiful, in a sense, for their under surface is thickly
coated with fine silky hairs which give it the whiteness of
oxydised silver.   The leaflets are coarsely toothed, and the
teeth end in silky hairs.   The plant has no stem, but produces its leaves—mostly lying flat—in a rosette round the
root-stock, and it sends off runners which root as they go, and
therefore you will always find the plant growing in congested

Oyster Mushroom.

colonies. The flowers have the neatness and symmetry exhibited by other species of *Potentilla,* and which has caused them to be largely used in ornament. The branching root-stock is not very stout, but it is said to be used as food in the Hebrides when other eatable things are scarce. We have never tried it, so cannot venture an opinion upon its virtues as a food-stuff.

But though we have never essayed a dish of Silverweed-roots, we can see an equally out-of-the-way food that we have tried, growing on the hedge-bank half a dozen yards off. A tree, probably an Elm, once grew there, but has been cut down, leaving a stump a few feet high, and this, bared of bark and hollowed in the centre, still produces a crop, though not of leaves. These be Vegetable Oysters, otherwise the Oyster Mushroom (*Pleurotus euosmus*); but we ought to explain that they are not so-called because of any resemblance in flavour or substance to the costly bivalve, but from some fancied resemblance of their upper sides to the slightly concave upper valve of the Oyster's shell. We have eaten it in the past, but we have tasted better mushrooms, and think that they look far prettier as they grow than when they are cooked and ready for consumption. In a broad sense the Oyster Mushroom is built after the fashion of the Common Mushroom—that is to say, it has a stem and a cap, and the underside of the cap bears " gills." But there is this great difference, that the stem instead of being central is lateral, and instead of shooting up from the ground it grows upon trees—usually much as you see it here, a number apparently growing one out of the other, and the gills running a good way down the stem. We are fortunate in finding it in such splendid condition for a photograph, and having obtained this you are quite free to carry the entire mass home and test its value as an esculent.

How to cook it, you ask ? Well, you have sufficient there to try it in several ways, but the generally accepted method for this kind is to stew slowly and gently until tender all through, adding such condiments and herbs as pleaseth your taste, and at the finish exercising similar discretion in the matter of gravy or sauce.   Let it be well understood that the pleasure of mushroom-eating largely depends upon the cooking, for, if this is injudiciously done, a mushroom that, fairly treated, would be tender and delicious may be made tough and indigestible.   It would be as well when interviewing the cook to say nothing as to these having grown upon wood, for there is an old-fashioned prejudice against mushrooms that have grown on or under trees.

Bramble.

False Cyperus.

"The River takes a sudden Curve."

JULY BY BOG AND STREAM.

BEGINNING our ramble where our last one left off, we make for the peaty hollow on the heath. There is a shallow pond, no doubt a bog in the making, for it has broad margins of peat, showing where once the pond extended. The successive generations of Bog-moss (*Sphagnum*), laced together by the fibrous rootlets of aquatic grasses and other plants, have gradually raised the level, and now it is like a saturated sponge which will not bear our weight without covering our feet with water.

Let us approach the water gradually, for there is a great quantity of vegetation around, and it is not without interest. For example, there are these large tufts like rank grasses, three or four feet in height. They are really a species of Sedge, and the Sedges (*Carex*) are a family few persons care to study, because the species are so numerous and at first sight so much alike. Of the British Carices alone there are

II.—K

over seventy species, and there are several allied genera that come very close to them, and these must be studied, too, in order to get a correct knowledge of the Sedges. But the particular kind we are looking at has the advantage for the tyro that it is very distinct from most of its relations. It is the False Cyperus (*Carex pseudo-cyperus*). It has a rough, three-sided stem, and broad flat leaves equally rough; but what gives charm to it are the flowers in long, pale green spikelets that droop in clusters on long foot-stalks. Each of these catkin-like spikelets is made up of a great number of flowers. The prickly appearance is due to the presence of bracts with long-toothed tips—in this family the bracts are known as *glumes*—in each of which reposes a flower, male *or* female. The male flowers consist merely of two or three stamens with no other covering than the glume. The females consist of a flattened or three-sided ovary enclosed in an urn-shaped covering (*perigynium*), from the mouth of which the stigmas project. The plant is called the False Cyperus because of its distant resemblance to the Paper Reed (*Cyperus papyrus*) of the Nile, whose pith was pressed and dried to provide the ancients with writing paper. In that case the spikelets radiate from the summit of a graceful stem twelve or fifteen feet high.

Well, here is—in its way—an equally striking plant, the Meadow Plume Thistle (*Cnicus pratensis*) — a thistle with just one solitary flower standing erect upon its round straight cottony stem. Judging solely by the leaves, no one would take it for a thistle, for they are soft and flat, without any of the long spines we usually associate with thistles. The whole plant appears to be covered with short cottony filaments. The lance-shaped leaves have their edges curiously cut into irregular lobes and teeth; the lower ones are stalked, but the few on the stem are stalkless, and with their eared bases clasping the stem. When the dark purple flower-head opens, it forms a very striking object. In order to get the whole plant upon our plate we have

Meadow Plume Thistle.

to reduce its proportions considerably—quite two-thirds. Speaking of this country generally, the plant is a rare one; but here, in north-west Surrey, it is fairly plentiful in wet places.

The strong smell of peppermint is due to your shoes crushing the plants of Water Mint (*Mentha hirsuta*) whose soft hairy leaves and spikes of purple flowers cover a wide extent of ground here. The Cotton-grass (*Eriophorum poly-*

Reeds and Rushes.

stachion) has been out some time, but its fleecy banners still wave in the breeze, though they are getting dull and tattered now. It is not a Grass but a Sedge, allied to the False Cyperus. The long cottony filaments surround the stamens and ovary in the flower and represent the calyx and corolla. Over there is a bright patch of rose colour at the edge of the water, which will interest you, for it is caused by the innumerable flowers of one of our most grace-ful plants. The Scarlet Pimpernel (*Anagallis arvensis*) of our cornfields is familiar to you, as to everyone else, for its reputation as the Poor Man's Weather-glass—a reputation not wholly well-founded — has made it thoroughly well known. But, however familiar the common species may be to us, it would scarcely occur to you that this was anything but a very distant relation, until you began a close examination. As a matter of fact this Bog Pimpernel (*Anagallis tenella*) is the only other distinct species of *Anagallis* we have in this country. We say "distinct species," because some authorities rank the blue-flowered variety of the Scarlet Pimpernel as a species; but if so it is not distinct, save in the matter of colour.

Here, however, you shall find a strong difference, not only in the colour, but also in the form of the flower, and in the size and disposition of the leaves, and the general "habit" of the plant. The Scarlet Pimpernel is an annual; this is a perennial. The stems of that are nearly two feet long; these are only about a fourth of that length, and the leaves of each are proportioned to the relative lengths of stem. But when we come to the flowers there is another tale to tell, for those of the Bog Pimpernel are at least as large as those of the Scarlet kind, and therefore they look hugely disproportionate to the stems and leaves. The oval or nearly round leaves are arranged in two opposite lines along the stems, and the funnel-shaped flowers are rosy, veined with crimson, and borne on long stout stalks. A pretty effect is produced in the flowers by the filaments of the stamens—which are all joined together by their bases— being densely clothed with long white hairs, the object of which is to exclude small pilferers.

The glossy round leaves which almost cover the ground here, and make it difficult to see the stems of Bog Pimpernel, belong to the Marsh Pennywort or White-rot (*Hydrocotyle vulgaris*), one of the smallest of our Umbelliferous plants. It is too small to photograph by itself, but you may be sure its leaves will show up in the portrait of Bog Pimpernel. The flowers are quite minute, and greenish with a tinge of pink. If you pluck one of the leaves and look at its underside you will see that the foot-stalk is attached to the centre of the leaf-disk. This constitutes the peltate form of leaf, which you will remember is the same in the Wall Pennywort (*Cotyledon umbilicus*), an unrelated plant (see vol. i. page 160). The name Marsh Pennywort is sufficiently explained by the shape of the leaf and the places where it grows. White-rot and Red-rot (one of the names of the Sundews) indicate a belief of agriculturists that feeding on these plants produced the disease of the liver in sheep which is known as the Rot. Such a disease is really induced in sheep pastured in marshy places, and it was perhaps natural that farmers of bygone days should attribute their trouble to such plants as they found there that do not grow on the upland pastures; but they were wholly mistaken. The poor plants were like prisoners often taken by the police, who have got to find someone guilty and so avenge outraged Law—they were on the spot at the time the mischief was done, and on this flimsy circumstantial evidence were convicted. It is well known now that the trouble is caused by an internal parasite (*Distomum hepatica*) that spends a part of its existence in the Marsh Snail (*Limnæa palustris*), which gets eaten by the sheep, when the *Distoma* makes its way to the sheep's liver and sets up the diseased condition. Unfortunately there are still many farmers who believe that these plants are the enemy.

We have mentioned the Sundew as the Red-rot, and here are vast numbers of its red rosettes among the fresh green Sphagnum. We have three species of Sundew in this country, and two of them are here present : the Round-leaved Sundew or Youthwort (*Drosera rotundifolia*) and the Intermediate Sundew (*Drosera intermedia*). Since Darwin published his famous work on *Insectivorous Plants*, thirty years ago, everybody has heard of the strange habits of the Sundews,

but most people appear to regard them as plants of considerable rarity—at anyrate not to be found in their own district.
The Round-leaved species is well distributed throughout the
country wherever there are bogs, and wet places on heaths.
On this heath if you go along the sandy track that does duty
for a road, and look into the ruts made by the wheels of the
waggon that last autumn carried fern, you will find them
covered with Sundews. And wherever there is a little
hollow or a slope that keeps the peaty soil moist, you will
find these plants growing thickly among the stems of Cross-
leaved Heath. Here, round the pond, they abound, and
extend down the heath-clad slope from the pine-wood above,
right to the water's edge. Some are even on the water itself,
buoyed up by floating moss and grass.

The Sundews have little root worth mentioning—just a
wisp of fibres that serves to steady them when they shoot up
the long thin flower-stems. From the thicker root-stock
above, the leaves extend all around in rosette-fashion; the
Round-leaved flat on the ground, the Intermediate erect, and
the Long-leaved taking a direction that is neither horizontal
nor vertical, but an inclination half-way between the two.
All the species, though differing in the shapes and attitudes
of their leaves, agree in having them thickly studded with
the red glandular hairs, each ending in a little knob from
which exudes a sticky fluid like liquid gum. Everybody
knows now that insects, mistaking these red-haired leaves
for flowers, settle upon them and get entrapped as surely as
the bird that perches on the bird-catchers' limed twigs. The
hairs are like the tentacles of the Sea Anemone: those in
contact with the captive telegraph the information to all the
others on the leaf, and they all bend their sticky knobs in the
direction of the disturbance, and all hold him down till he is
dead. Then the leaf pours a digestive fluid upon him which
dissolves all his soft parts. The resulting broth is absorbed
by the leaf and nourishes it. There you have the reason
why the Sundew sets up no elaborate system of roots. It

Bog Pimpernel.

gets its food in another way; and you can tell that the
business is a flourishing one by the crowds that are engaged
in it. The Sundews are insectivorous plants. A few years
ago one of our poets gave expression to his displeasure that
plants should develop such low tastes. He said—

> "What's this I hear
> About the new Carnivora?
> Can little plants
> Eat bugs and ants
> And gnats and flies?
> A sort of retrograding!
> Surely the fare of flowers is air,
> Or sunshine sweet.
> They shouldn't eat
> Or do aught so degrading."

The Sundews' flowers are rather poor affairs. They are
white and small, but are never much in evidence, as they do
not appear to remain open long—some, indeed, do not fully
open at all. The anthers and stigmas mature at the same
time, and self-fertilisation is certainly the rule. It is scarcely
to be expected that with the leaves putting on so flower-like
and attractive an appearance, the real flowers would have
much chance of attention from insects. There is indeed
direct competition between the two, if the flowers are
intended to be insect-fertilised; but we imagine that the
Sundews have given up the idea of anything but an occasional
cross, for the petals are very little longer than the sepals.
The flower-parts are very irregular in number, those of
Drosera intermedia varying from five to eight, whilst in
Drosera rotundifolia they are more frequently six.

Did you hear that strong shrill chirrup? There it is
again, sounding from that Sallow-bush. The sound is loud
enough for a Sparrow, but it is really produced by the Great
Green Grasshopper (*Locusta viridissima*). As we approach
the bush the chirrup is hushed, but having heard it before
we know what kind of creature it proceeds from, and a little
quiet inspection of the Sallow shows us the author of the

sound—a beautiful bright green Grasshopper, a couple of inches in length. His delicate antennæ are as long as his body, and the powerful leaping legs are longer still. Most of our Grasshoppers do not make their appearance until the grass is losing its bright tints, so they are soberly coloured with browns and greys mixed with the green; but this big fellow lives in the branches of bushes and trees—not entirely upon green - meat. The family is supposed to be purely

Great Green Grasshopper.

vegetarian, but entomologists who "sugar" the trees for moths have sometimes found this insect taking advantage of their labours by eating the bodies of the moths that have been rendered stupid by their indulgence in the spirituous syrup spread for their undoing. Of course, the entomologist who found himself thus cheated of his spoils by a big Grasshopper would be virtuously indignant. We kept one of these Great Green Grasshoppers as a pet a few years ago, and fed it entirely upon flies and other insects, which the Grasshopper

Round-Leaved Sundew,

took very prettily in his forelegs from between our fingers;
and after he had finished his supper he would treat us to
a chirruping performance of such power that it sounded
through the house. Only the males are musical.

If this peaty swamp were about a dozen miles farther
west, near the border of the county, we should discover
another of the floral beauties of such spots—one well fitted to
be the companion of the Bog Pimpernel and the Sundews.
This is the Ivy-leaved Bellflower (*Wahlenbergia hederacea*),
of which we can show you a photograph that represents it of
the natural size. It has a creeping underground root-stock,
from which it sends long thread-like stems in various
directions, bearing half-inch leaves that are five-lobed, much
after the fashion of an Ivy-leaf, but very thin and delicate,
of a beautiful pale green. Then, at about this season, you
would find a number of exquisite pale-blue flowers, not of
the ordinary bell-shape but cylindrical with a bell-shaped
opening where five little lobes stand up. These flowers
all stand erect on long and slender stalks, and the general
effect of the plant in flower is very charming. Always
keep an eye open for it when you are on moist peaty ground
in the proper localities—for it is a southern and western
plant, and does not occur farther north in England than
Yorkshire. In Scotland it appears again from Argyll to
Ayrshire.

Here is another of the Scorpion-grasses, growing near the
edge of the water, and forming a dense mass of yellow-
centred pale-blue flowers. It is the tufted Scorpion-grass
(*Myosotis cæspitosa*), and looks as though it might be a
small-flowered variety of the true Forget-me-not. It has
got bright green shining leaves like the Forget-me-not, but
its flowers are only one-third of the diameter of *Myosotis
palustris*, and its stems are all more or less upright, growing
in a tuft a couple of feet high. It sends out no runners like
the Forget-me-not, and its stems and branches are not
nearly so stout. Seen in the mass its flowers are wonder-

fully effective. We cannot photograph the whole clump, for to get such a mass on our plate would necessitate so great a reduction that the small flowers would be lost entirely, so we must be content with a portion, and to get that we must wait patiently, for the breeze keeps its branches well on the move.

Yellow Flags.

The beauty of the Ragged Robin (*Lychnis flos-cuculi*) has passed, but there are still a few flowers left on its long slender branches; and so with the clump of Yellow Flags (*Iris pseudacorus*) that stand like an island out in the pool. These things we have met with on our earlier rambles; but here is a plant that is likely to be overlooked until it is in flower. All round the swamp and along

Ivy-Leaved Bellflower.

riversides there is a great quantity of foliage, that at a distance is very much alike—long, slender, strap-like leaves, that only call attention to their considerable differences when flowers begin to appear. Some of the sword-shaped leaves, that you thought were Iris, again turn out to belong to the Sweet Flag (*Acorus calamus*), a relation of Cuckoo-pint. Then these softer straps that are flattened in the other direction, and whose upper ends droop more or less, you might suppose to belong to Reed-mace (*Typha latifolia*) or Bulrush (*Scirpus lacustris*), but the clump includes both these and Bur-reed (*Sparganium ramosum*) as well. When people speak of Bulrush they generally mean Reed-mace, and when they point to the Bulrushes that line the stream before the flowering time, it is more frequently the foliage of Sparganium that has misled them. Sparganium is related to the Reed-mace, and as it is at present in flower you may make yourself acquainted with it whilst we select a spray of its flowers — or part of a spray—for photographing. Like many other things we try to employ the camera upon, there is really too much of it. The studio-photographer has no difficulty with these social plants, for he just gathers as much as he wants and takes it home to pose. But as our object is, as far as possible, to depict the growing plant in the place where it grows, we sometimes lose distinctness owing to the great number of specimens that will obtrude themselves where we only want one or part of one. These leaves that come from the root are far too long. If we get their five-feet lengths upon our six-inch plate, the one-inch burs will be reduced to very minute dimensions. Well, here is a flowering branch, part of which must suit our purpose, and we will be content with such portions of the leaves as will come in. At this distance the reduction will be about three-fourths, so our burs will only come out at a quarter of their natural size. That is done: and now let us examine these burs for your benefit, for they are really clusters of flowers. This is an example of a plant that bears separate male and female flowers on the same spike. The upper clusters are assemblages of male flowers only, and if you pick one of them to pieces you will find that the individual flowers have neither calyx nor corolla—the *perianth,* which represents both, consists of a few thin scales, enclosing two or three stamens. The female head is similarly made up, but instead of the flowers containing stamens there is just one ovary which tapers off into a simple style. It develops after fertilisation into a single-seeded, egg-shaped drupe with a little beak.

If you follow one of these long leaves down to its attachment to the root-stock, you will find that it becomes thick, three-sided, and keeled along the back. These shorter "leaves" that run out horizontally below each spike of flowers are really bracts.

The low herbage around the pool is "alive" with thousands of young toads that have not yet strayed far from their birthplace. The next heavy rains will probably scatter them far and wide upon the heath. But if we are to enjoy a stroll along the riverside after we reach its banks, we must leave this spot.

Setting our faces northward we push through the thick heath plants, and through the belt of pine-woods, and out upon another stretch of heath, where we come upon several rather extensive clumps of Hemp Nettle (*Galeopsis tetrahit*), with bristly stems three feet high, large nettle-like leaves, and two-lipped rosy flowers in dense whorls. It is a plant we should sooner have expected to find round some cornfield, but it is quite at home here, and there are some curious insects at home upon it. They are quaint green creatures with a margin of spines along each side, and two long spines for a tail, which they turn over their backs and on them support a good deal of rubbish which forms a kind of umbrella. Whether this is to shelter them from sun and rain, or to make them unpalatable to insectivorous birds, does not appear, but it makes them look odd. They are

Common Hemp Nettle.

Tufted Scorpion-Grass.

Branched Bur-Reed.

really the larval forms of the Great Tortoise-beetle (*Cassida equestris*), and if we come along here about a fortnight later we shall find they have attained to full beetle-hood, rather flattened greenish creatures with slightly convex wing-covers that suggest *the* tortoise. It is a beetle that we are accustomed to find more frequently upon Thistles.

Now just along this short lane, whose banks are covered with Tufted Vetch (*Vicia cracca*) in full flower, and Tansy (*Tanacetum vulgare*) with its solid-looking buds still unopened; and here we are upon the river-bank.

> "On a sudden a low breath
> Of tender air made tremble in the hedge
> The fragile Bindweed-bells and Bryony rings."

And here is a plant that we have met in the meadows, but always too late in the day, when its flowers had closed. This is the Goat's-beard (*Tragopogon pratensis*) whose other name is John-go-to-bed-at-noon. These are rather small specimens, but it is a very variable plant, for sometimes its heads are a couple of inches across whilst at other times they measure no more than half an inch. These are intermediate between these extremes. Note how much longer the involucral bracts are than the strap-shaped corollas, so that, if you have hitherto only seen the plant when its heads were closed up for the day, you would expect to find them much larger when open than they are. It is getting towards the end of the season for the Goat's-beard now, but having seen it you are not likely to overlook it another season. It is a common complaint that many of the yellow Composite plants are so much alike in their flower-heads, and that it is difficult to remember the differences between Cat's-ears and Hawkweeds and Hawk's-beards; but Goat's-beard at least is rendered sufficiently distinct by its glaucous rush-like leaves, and these long involucral bracts.

For a time we walk under trees, whose long arms thrown across the water almost meet those from the other side.

Now the river takes a sudden but wide curve to the left and comes out from under the trees, and we get all the immediate surroundings reflected in the clear waters.

There is much to interest us here—Bur-reed and Bulrush again in plenty along the margins, fishes in the stream and

Goat's Beard.

patient anglers sitting beneath the Willows trying to snare them. And then we come to a little bay where we can look more comfortably into the water and watch the snails that glide over the bottom and up the stems of the water-weeds. There are some especially noticeable because they are just the shape of Winkles, only much larger, with striped shells.

Marsh Woundwort.

They are the River Snail (*Vivipara vivipara*), a species that, like one of the marine Winkles, retains its eggs until they have hatched, and so produces its young alive. Though the shell is much thinner than that of the Winkle—being horny rather than stony, which is a condition only necessary for the rough-and-tumble life of the seashore—this River Snail agrees with the Winkle in having a horny door that fits the mouth of the shell when the snail wishes privacy and seclusion. But there is a mollusk of much larger proportions here. Look at the bottom there and you will make out the gaping shells of huge mussels—not the mussel of salt-water, but the Swan Mussel (*Anodonta cygnœa*), which is purely a fresh-water form. They are packed pretty closely, and their numbers in that colony must be considerable. Some enemy has been at them, for there are many broken shells here on the bank. Some of these measure seven inches in length by four inches deep, with a thickness of two inches and a half. A fairly substantial meal.

But we must not forget the plants. This is the month when riverside vegetation is at its best. The Meadow-sweet is not yet over, though it has lost its first freshness and fulness, and the tow-rope has broken much of it down. But there is sufficient left to make it a noticeable feature of the landscape, and there are many newly-flowered species to give variety. Here is a common, but little known, plant of watery places— the Marsh-Woundwort (*Stachys palustris*), a near ally of the Hedge-Woundwort (*Stachys sylvatica*), a plant that is conspicuous now by copse-sides and hedgerows. This is very similar to that, except that it is of rather smaller stature, the leaves narrower, the hairs softer, the flowers a paler purple, and the odour from the bruised stem less objectionable. The stem you observe, as is characteristic of plants with Labiate flowers, is square, and, as usual with Labiates, the leaves are in pairs on opposite sides of the stem. The plant ends in a long raceme, the flowers arranged in whorls of eight or ten with a little interval between each whorl.

These plants had formerly a prodigious reputation, primarily, as the name suggests, for the cure of wounds, but secondarily as universal remedies. The modern pill-man who advertises a nostrum that is equally effective in a case of broken limbs as in a cold or a stomach derangement understands human credulity, and knows that in these matters the race is as gullible as it was in the time of the Cæsars. Culpepper quotes the opinion of Antony Muse, who was physician to Octavius, as to the virtues of Woundwort. It is too long to quote, but we would commend it to the attention of the gentlemen who write the advertisements of Blank's Pills; it would probably give them a point or two. He winds up by saying, "It is a very precious herb, that is certain, and most fitting to be kept in a man's house, both in syrup, conserve, oil, ointment, and plaister."

We have little doubt that for some few of the ills on Antony Muse's list Woundwort is an admirable remedy, and possibly preferable to the mysterious prescriptions of a modern medicine-man who has all the approved qualifications; but our own prescription would be an instruction to get out into the places where these herbs grow as a means of improving impaired health.

This piece of swampy ground is crowded with vegetation. Much of it we have already met with, and some things we are sure to find along the banks; but there is a plant with clustered masses of tiny pale pink flowers whose height forces itself upon our attention. It is the Cat's Valerian or All-Heal (*Valeriana officinalis*), and some of its stems are five and six feet high. Its long, broad leaves are very fine, being divided into a number of paired lance-shaped leaflets with toothed edges. Root-leaves and stem-leaves are alike, except that the former, of course, are much larger. The individual flowers though insignificant in point of size are yet worth examining. The calyx is represented by a thickened ring at the base of the funnel-shaped corolla-tube, but after the flower has been fertilised the calyx ring unrolls and develops

Cat's Valerian.

into a sort of feathered shuttlecock. The corolla, which is only about one-sixth of an inch across, has five lobes which are not equal in size, and there are only three stamens which mature before the stigma. The flowers produce honey, which, owing to the shortness of the tube, is accessible to insects with short tongues, and seeing that all flowers are not open to the short-tongued these are well patronised. The root and leaves have a peculiar odour which is monstrously pleasing to cats. If they can get at it they will eat of the root or chew the leaves, and it is said to be equally seductive to rats, and that rat-catchers enlist its aid in the prosecution of their profession. The *officinalis* of its name implies that it has been admitted to regular use in medicine; and it is still prescribed in hysteria and nervous complaints. By the way, these plants before us have the leaflets toothed all round, and therefore it must be the var. *sambucifolia*; the typical specimens have the leaflets toothed on one side only.

In the stream just here is a colony of Arrow-head (*Sagittaria sagittifolia*), so-called on account of the form of the leaves. Look at the plant well whilst we photograph it, and you will see that though all the leaves have this arrow-head form, it yet permits of a great deal of variety, some being broad and proportionately short, whilst others are slender with the lateral lobes very long. It is a perennial plant, and at the bottom of the water the thick stem sends out runners. At the end of each runner a bud forms, and late in autumn all the material from these large leaves and stems will be carried down and packed into these buds, which will be greatly enlarged, of course, by the process. Then when spring stirs the plant into activity each of these buds will start as an independent plant. The first leaves they put forth, will not come into the air, and to make them more fitted for aquatic existence they will be exceedingly slender, and so thin in texture that you can see clearly through them. The next leaves come up to the surface and lie upon it like Water-lily leaves, and these you will note are broad and less pointed.

Lastly come up the aerial leaves on longer stalks, and these are much more slender and more truly the shape of arrow-heads, with long pointed barbs extending backwards. Finally come the flowers, which are arranged in whorls on the flower-stem. You see that there are only three sepals and three petals, and that the latter are white except at the base, where they narrow into a claw which is purple, and the anthers of the numerous stamens are also purple. Another point to notice is that the two sexes are in separate flowers: the upper ones with longer stalks containing stamens only and the lower ones pistils only. Arrow-head extends north only as far as Cumberland.

Just ahead there is a near relation of the Arrow-head and a plant of much wider distribution. It is the so-called Water Plantain (*Alisma plantago*). It has no connection with *the* Plantains, though when not in flower the man in the street would be justified in supposing it is one of them, for its conspicuously ribbed, large oval leaves are much like those of the Greater Plantain (*Plantago major*). Some of these leaves you see are not far short of a foot long, but they have much longer leaf-stalks than the Plantain has. Now that we have the plant in flower there is no excuse for anyone mistaking it for a Plantain. The flower-stem runs up to a length of three feet or more, sending out long branches in whorls, and these again have whorls, but of flower-stalks. The flowers are formed on exactly the same lines as those of the Arrow-head, only they are much smaller, and of a delicate rose or lilac tint. The flowers of the Arrow-head were few in number; here there are so many that to number them would be a task, and the tips of all the shoots and the extremity of the main stem have many more buds in embryo, to keep up a succession for another month. We have said that the flowers are like those of Arrow-head, but this requires one qualification: there are both stamens and pistils in each flower, but the stamens are reduced in number to six.

Arrow-Head.

In photographing the Water Plantain one would get a finer result if we could come across a single plant with just one flowering stem; but the rule is for them to grow in groups, and the branches of the several stems get mixed up and confused.

We have said a good deal about Reeds in a general and collective sense, but so far have omitted to point out to you *the* Reed (*Arundo phragmites*), although we have passed by many plants of it just coming into flower. Here is a clump with the purple-brown panicles of flowers issued from their sheaths and nodding like silky plumes. Now the Reed, unlike all these reed-like plants we have been considering, is a true grass—the largest of our native grasses, growing often to a height of ten feet. It has a thick perennial rootstock that creeps in the mud or earth and sends up very erect stout rounded stems. It has long flat leaves of a harsh character, sometimes an inch in width, with stiff bristly edges that cut like a razor if injudiciously handled. The panicle is a foot to a foot and a half long, of an oval shape, with long silky hairs among the flowers. The smooth polished spikelets contain three or four flowers each, which are of the usual grass type, with flowering glumes and empty glumes. There are three stamens, and the short styles end in feathery stigmas.

It is customary to describe the Reed as a water-weed whose habitat is the margin of lakes and the banks of rivers. This is so far correct, but it also grows in great abundance where its roots cannot be in water. Many of the Cornish cliffs produce fine crops of Reeds, which are locally known as Goss, and are used for thatching the few cottages that have not yet taken to a corrugated iron roof. The latter has not been preferred out of any desire for its peculiar style of artistic beauty, but because it is less likely to burn in the case of fire. As a growing plant the Reed is very valuable for its quality of binding the sands on the shore at the base of the cliffs, where the fresh waters that percolate

through the cliff and come out at its base serve it instead of
the waters of lake or river.

It is no less decorative when in flower than the more
popular Reed-mace (*Typha latifolia*), and we remember well
the important part it played in the decorations of a coast
village on the occasion of the Diamond Jubilee. The
villagers went off in boats at early morn to gather the
material along the cliffs, and when the procession of boats
filed into the "porth," laden high with "Goss" and flowers,
the sight was an exceedingly picturesque one.

Speaking of *Typha*, there are several plants here of the
smaller species (*Typha angustifolia*), which is just pushing
up its poker-like cylindrical spikes from the shelter of the
sheathing leaves. We have already referred to the common
mistake that is made in calling this and its larger relative
(*Typha latifolia*) Bulrushes; other names that really belong
to it in different localities are Cat's-tail and Club-rush. The
leaves form two rows, and are long slender straps much like
those of Bur-reed. The flowers, too, are essentially the same
as in Bur-reed, but arranged differently. There are, indeed,
two spikes one above the other on the same stalk. The
upper and yellow one consists of male flowers which
ultimately fall off. The lower and dark-brown one contains
the female flowers and fruit, and the latter remain. This
Smaller Reed-mace is not as widely distributed as the larger
species. Like others of these reed-like plants, its leaves and
stems are used for thatching and similar purposes.

A common, but little known, plant by the riverside is this
Bur-Marigold (*Bidens cernua*) with its succulent branched
stem and connected pairs of lance-shaped leaves. It is a
Composite plant, and its dull brownish-yellow heads nod on
their stalks. All its flowers are tubular like those of Tansy,
so the heads are not very conspicuous. Rarely, we may find
a plant whose heads have a few short rays. The fruits
terminate in four fine, sharp bristles which have barbed tips.
These are intended to catch and hold in the fur of animals

and so get disseminated far from the parent plant. This office is well performed, and often, after you have walked beside the river (where you may not have noticed the plant), you will find a number of these sticking tightly to the lower portions of your dress. It has been put on record that Gold-fish have been killed by these seeds attaching themselves in numbers to the gills and jaws, and preventing the proper

"A Dense Wall of Reeds."

action of these parts. The naturalist who uses a net to catch snails, beetles, and other small creatures, by drawing it through the water-weeds, often finds it partially covered with these tenacious seeds.

Is not this a charming part of the stream? Behind us deep pine-woods, where the apparently endless masses of Willow-herb fill the spaces between the trees with a rosy glow that disperses their gloom. Before us the still waters covered with the large floating leaves of Water-lilies, and here

and there, raised well above the stream, the almost globular
flowers of the Yellow Water-lily (*Nymphœa lutea*) or Brandy
Bottle.   On the other side of the stream a dense wall of
reeds of various kinds, and at their feet here and there one
can see that the Buckbean's flowering time has not yet
passed.   There are other things one can see in those masses
of reed beyond, but until we come across their like on this
side the stream, we had better say nothing about them.
Shall we come across them, you ask ?   Oh yes ; we know
the stream sufficiently well to guarantee them, unless perchance some flower gatherer has been along before us and
stripped the banks of their beauty.   But that is not likely,
for here it is only the angler, the entomologist, and other
lovers of Nature that come.   Look at those Lilies !   If this
were a haunt of the ordinary destroying tripper, he would
get a boat from somewhere, or failing that would swim or
wade out, and gather every one of those flowers and disfigure
the place generally.

Talking of swimming or wading—is not the sight of that
placid water, with its wonderful reflections of reeds and trees
and fleecy clouds, sufficient this warm day to tempt one to
plunge in ?   It is surely the place to find the answer to
Browning's question—

> " Oh, which were best, to roam or rest ?
> The land's lap or the water's breast ?
> To sleep on yellow millet-sheaves,
> Or swim in lucid shallows, just
> Eluding water-lily leaves . . .
> Which life were best on Summer eves ? "

There are the Water-lilies intact, and there is no sign of
recent disturbance.   We cannot get sufficiently near to ob-
tain anything approaching a life-sized representation, but the
flowers will be distinct enough with a four-fifth's reduction,
and the leaves in their natural haphazard arrangement will
come in too ; whilst a view of the farther side will give an
idea of the extent of the Lily-beds.   And here in the fore-

Water Plantain.

ground are a couple of leaves just making their appearance
from below. These illustrate what botanists term the
vernation of the plant. The leaves at first are tightly rolled
up from the two sides inwards to the midrib. When they

A Lily Pond in the Woods.

reach the surface both sides unroll and lie flat upon the
water. Never again will their upper surfaces get wet.
Their thick leathery substance is coated with a waxy
covering on which water seems to have an objection to
stay. The slight shower a few minutes ago fell upon

them, as upon the stream, but see how the little globules of water have rolled to the edges without making the leaf wet. And the first time a breeze comes along and ruffles the stream, the rocking of the leaves will shake those crystal drops clean off. There are other leaves below the water that are not intended to come to the surface. These are of much thinner texture.

The large and massive appearance of the flower is due solely to the five or six golden sepals. There are a great number of petals—nearly twenty—but these are so small that they look like stamens. The carpels are all united into a big central ovary—something after the manner of the same parts in the Poppy—with the stigmas likewise united into a circular plate with hollow centre and turned-down edges. If you look at the surface of this disk you will see it is marked with a large number of lines radiating from the centre. These are the stigmas. You will find the stamens springing from under the edge of the disk; they are very slender. There is something analogous to the Hellebores in the petals—those we found in the case of Setterwort had been converted into tubular nectaries. These are not tubular, but each petal bears a gland near its extremity which produces honey. The flowers are what are called fragrant, but the odour is distinctly spirituous, which has led to its alternative name of Brandy Bottle.

We are fortunate in finding, at no distance apart, repre-sentatives of our two native genera of Water Lilies, for there, not a hundred yards ahead, are a few flowers of the White Water-lily (*Castalia speciosa*). Yes, we expected you to ask why two plants so much alike and differing only in the colours of their flowers should be put into different genera? But are they so much alike as to warrant inclusion in one genus? That is the question. Superficially they are alike, and probably if there were no flowers out you would be unable to say which is Yellow Lily and which White. But get a flower of each, and look into them,

Yellow Water-Lily.

and you will admit that the differences are far more than
are visible on a cursory examination from a little distance.
First of all, there are only four sepals; and though they
are white inside they are green outside, so that the unopened
buds are green. Then, the large number of petals show
every gradation, from the full size down to the most slender
proportions. The stamens too have tried to turn themselves
into petals, so that we have some of them as wide as
the narrowest petals but ending in anthers. The Yellow
Water-lily never opens widely: the White one spreads its
sepals until they touch the water, and the outer rows of
petals lie upon them, but the inner ones are erect. This
difference of attitude gives the open flower a very full and
rose-like appearance. Another difference of habit may be
seen in the ripening of the seed-vessels. The Yellow Water-
lily holds her head above the water all the time; but the
White Water-lily after fertilisation withdraws beneath the
surface and ripens her seeds under water.

What a different effect is produced by a change in the
lighting. When we photographed the Yellow Water-lily
the sky was overcast, for a shower had just fallen, and the
leaves will come out not much lighter than the water. Now,
note the effect of a strong top light on the leaves of these
White Lilies. The sky is blue and the clouds have passed.
Every leaf is shining with light, and just below the rim of
each, just lifted from the water, there is so intense a shadow
that the leaves look as though they were not real but had
been strongly outlined in black. That effect will also
appear in the photograph.

The swampy bit of heath on our left is suffused with a
rosy hue, from the great quantity of Cross-leaved Heath in
flower; but nearer at hand it is golden with the blossoms
of the Dwarf Furze (*Ulex nanus*), that has just come into
flower and will continue for several months. The Dwarf
Furze is a lowly plant that has recumbent stems which
cover the ground where it grows as with a barbed wire

entanglement. Though the stems may be as much as three feet in length they seldom rise more than a few inches above the ground, and persons properly attired for walking—as we are—in knickerbockers, get severely punished for walking through it. The spines are not so rigid as in the Common Furze, but that grows as a bush which we can avoid. The Dwarf Furze covers the ground completely, and cannot be avoided if you must walk over the area it has marked out for its own. Every step you take means a vicious stab of a stiletto into your ankles, and though for a time you may determine to brave it out, it is probable that you will soon make up your mind that your business really lies on that other part of the heath where all is rosy rather than golden. We have been in it often before, but have no desire just now to repeat the experience. That is no reason why you should not try it, and maybe you would be rewarded by finding the Dwarf Willow (*Salix repens*), which grows over yonder along the ground, and has slender lance-shaped silky leaves.

There goes the Red Admiral Butterfly (*Vanessa atalanta*), one of the commonest of insects at this season, and one of the most showy that we have. The broad bands of brilliant scarlet running diagonally across the velvety black forewings, which are finely edged and spotted with white, and the black-dotted, broader bands of scarlet on the hinder wings, make it very conspicuous. This is probably its first flight, for the Admirals do not emerge from the chrysalis much before August, when they become plentiful. We may be fortunate enough to see him settle on a Thistle-head, and then would be a good opportunity to photograph him. Attempts of this sort, however, involve much loss of time with few results, the butterflies, being able to see all round at once, are off again before you can focus them. Ah! he has settled on that spray of Heath, so he has probably already refreshed at the sign of the Thistle. Got him! though he kept his wings folded together and only showed the underside of them. But what a marvellous piece of

White Water-Lily.

decoration that underside is, although little more than a series of lines in grey, brown, black and pink, wonderfully blended and harmonised.

Just look at these tall grass-stems! About one in every four is ornamented by a one-sided, spindle-shaped cocoon of shining yellow papery material. They are the cocoons of the Six-spot Burnet Moth (*Zygœna filipendulœ*), and through their tissues you can dimly distinguish the form of a black chrysalis in some. Others have the empty chrysalis skin protruding from the upper end, showing that the moth has escaped. And here are hundreds of the beautiful moths lazily flitting about in the sunshine and settling on the Thistle-heads.

Red Admiral Butterfly.

Gaudy creatures they are, as the sun falls upon their metallic-looking upper wings of very dark green relieved by six crimson spots; whilst the under-wings are of the same crimson tint, save for a narrow border of black. Their long, thick, club-shaped antennæ and their bodies are coloured dark metallic green to match their upper wings. They are much given to guzzling, which they regard as so serious a business that, when engaged upon it, you may pluck the flower from which they are imbibing without disturbing them in the least. Some few years ago, in Cornwall, we plucked a Scabious head upon which were no fewer than six of these moths, their heads close together. The Scabious was stuck in our buttonhole, and we walked five miles home across the cliffs, and when we entered the house there were five Burnet Moths still quiet upon the flower.

An entomologist is busy netting these moths, but we notice that after a critical examination most of them are set free again. He is selecting the very best specimens, or perhaps seeking for some special variety.

Here is a fine plant, four or five feet in height, that has some very lowly relations. It is the Yellow Loosestrife (*Lysimachia vulgaris*), a species peculiar to riversides and similar wet situations, whose nearest connections in this country are the Woodland Loosestrife (*Lysimachia nemorum*) and the Creeping Jenny (*Lysimachia nummularia*). Those are quite unassuming plants, that creep among other humble herbs and make no effort to thrust themselves upon public attention. But this stately plant, with its very straight stems and fine golden head, is not one that can be easily overlooked. Like its smaller relations it has a creeping root-stock, but from this it sends up erect downy stems with fine, long, lance-shaped, black-dotted leaves, given off in pairs. The black dots are glands. From the axils of the upper leaves spring out long flowering branches, also erect, ending in a cyme of bright yellow flowers dotted with orange. The corolla is of the so-called wheel-shape (*rotate*) order, with five egg-shaped lobes, and the calyx lobes are bordered with red and fringed.

The Lysimachia genus is a branch of the Primrose family; therefore, knowing what we do of the "pin-eyed" and "thrum-eyed" flowers in the Common Primrose and Cowslip, we are not surprised to find that there are two forms of flower in this Yellow Loosestrife. This plant before us is the short-styled form. The flowers produce no honey, but they are regularly visited—as you see—by bees: it is to be presumed for pollen.

Yellow Loosestrife.

Flowering Rush.

See what a beautiful effect is produced by the breeze on that Osier-bed that runs beside the stream ahead of us. The wind blows from us, and as it bends every pliant Osier rod it turns up the silvery-white under-sides of the leaf to view, and the whole plantation suddenly changes from bright green to white. Beyond, on the other side of the stream, there is a sequestered meadow, tree-surrounded, where the

The Breeze on the Osier-Bed.

cattle would like to get down to the water, and the wire fence is intended to keep them from it, though it looks like a difficulty that can be—and probably has been—surmounted. It is an illustration of Charles Mackay's lines—

> "The panting beeves
> Cool the hoof and switch the tail,
> And gaze upon the waters pale
> With mild eyes grateful for the shade
> By the o'erarching verdure made."

We are passing agricultural land now, and thick hedges

take the place of heath and wood for a time, but there are many wild things in the hedgerow and at its foot, if we had time to sort them out from the tangle; for the bridge that will enable us to cross the stream, and so take the short-cut home, is some distance ahead still.

There is yet another tall plant we had hoped to see in flower, and we remember that in former years we have found it near this spot as well as in many places we have passed. But until the flowers are out, it is so easy to overlook the Flowering Rush (*Butomus umbellatus*) among the plants of similar reed-like growth along the crowded margins of the river.   We appear to be close upon it at last, for that touch of rosy colour above the reedy marge can be nothing else. Here it is, but the fine umbel consists chiefly of unexpanded buds.   Still, on the *ex pede Herculem* principle, there is sufficient not only for identification, but also to give an idea of what a fine display there is when an umbel is fully expanded.   There is another little surprise for you when you learn that this plant is nearly related to Water Plantain and Arrow-head, so different does it appear in the shape of the leaves, the form and colour of the flowers.   The shape of the leaves is quite a small matter, for those of Arrow-head are utterly unlike those of the Water Plantain; therefore, we might reasonably expect another relation to have leaves like or unlike either.   The more imposing character of the inch-wide flowers in *Butomus* is due first to the fact that the floral leaves are developed to a larger size, and next to the sepals being coloured and of equal size and shape with the petals.   Then the stamens and pistils are coloured red also, and instead of the flowers being scattered they are all brought together in a cluster.

The leaves appear to be mimetic.   You know that many of the Sedge family have their long slender leaves either three-sided, or if flat have a raised keel along the back. The three-sided form we also found in Bur-reed, and there is no doubt it is a form well suited for the situations where

Winter Cress.

these plants grow, for it gives backbone, so to speak, to a
long slender leaf without making it too rigid. Well, as
you see, the leaves of the Flowering Rush are three-sided,
and when you measure up these before you and find they
vary between three and four feet in length, you will understand that they need strengthening somewhere to enable
them to maintain the erect attitude.

"Where the Cattle would like to get down to the Water."

And here is the bridge that spans the stream, and the
presence of the children on the banks shows that we have
reached the abodes of men once more. Before we leave the
waterside just note this dark-green plant with angular stem
and glossy foliage. Though it has been in flower since May,
and we have come across it before, we have never photographed it, and its flowering time will be over in a week or
two. This is the Winter Cress (*Barbarea vulgaris*), so-called
not because it flowers in winter—which is not the case—but
because its leaves are available for salad purposes at the end
and beginning of the year when most other edible herbs are

wanting. Not that it is so used to-day; but in other days, when we had no cultivation under glass, nor the products of milder climes brought rapidly to our markets, it was held in some esteem. To-day it would probably be considered too tough for the purpose, our masticatory powers having degenerated as our intellects have been developed. It is a Cruciferous plant but slightly separated from the Water Cress (*Nasturtium officinale*), and partaking of the virtues of that herb. The lower leaves are pinnate, much like those of the Water Cress; but whereas the small flowers of that are white, in Winter Cress they are larger and bright yellow, borne in dense terminal racemes. In former times it was apparently also known as Black Cress owing to the darkness of its green, for the description of the plant of that name given by Culpepper agrees with this. It grows in all sorts of places, solitary plants being often found by the roadside and in wastes, but by the waterside you will find it not singly but often in considerable crowds—as here—and when many plants are in flower together it makes a fine patch of colour.

The End of a Waterside Ramble.

Cow Parsnip or Hogweed.

A Field Corner.

AUGUST IN THE FIELDS.

WHEN the grass was cut in the meadows a great number of our subjects went with it to make hay; but although the reaping machine disposed of all the tall-growing things, like Buttercups and Dog Daisies, it did not cut so close as to take off all the trailing stems of Clover and other lowly plants. We have had some refreshing rains since the hay was carried, and many things have not only sent out new shoots, but are flowering afresh. Besides, the extreme margins and the corners of the fields, and many a bit of roadside waste, have not been touched by the mowers, and these just now are crowded with various weeds of the more rampant kinds. Although many of these are fine bold subjects for the camera, we are still not happy, because there is the feeling that we have to sacrifice so much in order to get whole plants upon our plates. We are like the farmers—always have cause for grumbling. With them, if prices are good the crop is not heavy enough; and if the crop is large the prices are so low, it is not worth sending to market. With us, if the plants are small we cannot get near enough to them to take them in comfort, and if they are large we are compelled to stand so far back that fine details are lost by the reduction in size. Still, like the farmers, we shall probably get a fair average.

Here is a magnificent Cow Parsnip or Hogweed (*Heracleum sphondylium*), standing by the hedge, and towering something over six feet. Its lower leaves are at least a yard long, cut up into several leaflets and these again boldly lobed. The stout, hollow stems are strongly grooved and covered with short, stiff, whitish hairs. From the axils of the stem-leaves long straight shoots are given off, and these only fail to be erect in order to avoid collision with the great compound umbel which terminates the main stem, for each of these minor shoots is ending in a less extensive compound umbel. For an Umbelliferous plant the flowers are large—more especially the irregular outer row of each umbel. They are also very numerous; in this specimen pale pink, but often white. What a fine show could be made of a dozen such plants in the shrubbery! But for this purpose a still larger species (*Heracleum villosum*) from the Caucasus is used, which stands ten or twelve feet high. Our Cow Parsnip when it grows beside the road is rather a vagabondish-looking plant, for the broad rough leaves gather a great quantity of road dust; but here, in the field, it is a much more presentable plant. Note what a fine effect is produced by the base of the leaf-stalk spreading out into a broad, pale, concave sheath that partly wraps the stem. Its common names indicate that it is a good food-plant for various animals. Cobbett experimented with it in the feeding of horses, and was satisfied by the results obtained that it was a valuable forage plant.

The flowers are succeeded by flat, shield-shaped fruits which, on account of their superior size, should be care-

Bird's-foot Trefoil.

fully examined if you wish to get a good idea of the fruits in this large family of plants. They are a quarter of an inch wide, flat, but one side is slightly convex. Each flower produces two of them, and they are remarkably poised from their upper ends on a branched bristle known as the carpophore. They have thin wings round the edges, and the rounded face is marked with five raised lines between which are four curved, club-shaped, brown marks. These are internal tubes filled with the aromatic oil which makes the fruits of many Umbellifers useful in medicine and cookery. The stems when young and juicy are edible, and have a pleasant flavour suggestive partly of carrot, partly of celery. Try it!

Before we leave, note how fond the honey-bee is of the flowers. Bees have been coming and going all the time we have been looking at this plant, and there is one on almost each of the umbels round about us. But the Cow Parsnip, like most of the Umbelliferæ, spreads its nectar on plates, so that all classes of insect-life can avail themselves of it, and so we find Blue-bottle and Green-bottle, and even small beetles, enjoying it. No wonder that the plants of this family appear in such great numbers when they press so many kinds of insects into their service.

And here creeping among the grass, where it has been brightening the meadows for the last two months, is the pretty little Bird's-foot Trefoil (*Lotus corniculatus*), or Lady's Slipper as it is often called. Like Cow Parsnip, it is a plant that appears commonly throughout the length and breadth of these islands, so that it does not require searching for. It is a perennial plant with a woody root-stock, from which branch out a number of tough, angled, and twisted branching stems. The leaves, which are divided into three or (mostly) five smooth oval leaflets, are of a dark dull green. From their axils are produced the wiry flower-stems, four or five inches long, bearing a head of about six bright yellow flowers. In bud these appear to

be red owing to the standard or large upper petal being
coloured red on the outer side, and on the inside there is a
central hair-line of red running from the base to the margin,
and on either side of it there are several shorter, very fine
lines converging to the entrance to the flower. The pollen
is shed into the "keel" of the flower before the bud opens,
and the pressure of a bee's body upon the wings forces the
pollen out upon the bee's underside, much as in Furze and
the other Leguminous flowers we have noted. The general
effect of these flowers as they grow among the turf is very
much like that of the small yellow Calceolaria of the garden.
The flowers are succeeded by long cylindrical pods, over an
inch long, and the appearance of several of these radiating
from the stem is very like that of a bird's foot, and here
you have the explanation of the plant's name.

Another yellow flower of the Leguminous order, that is
very liable to be passed over by the casual rambler as Bird's-
foot Trefoil, is this Yellow Pea (*Lathyrus pratensis*). Of
course, the merest examination will show marked differences,
but the thing that strikes the non-botanical is the size and
colour of the flowers, and the fact that in so many places
the two species grow side by side, as here. But, leaving the
flowers out of account for the moment, here we have sharply
angled stems, two or three feet long, partly trailing and
partly climbing by means of tendrils, which are really the
midrib of the leaf adapted as a prehensile organ. The
leaf is represented by a pair of lance-shaped leaflets, and
at the base of the leaf-stalk there is a pair of large
arrow-shaped stipules which no doubt act as leaflets to
make up for so much of the leaf material having been
converted into tendrils. These tendrils cling to grasses,
brambles, or whatever else may offer as supports. The
flower head is mounted on a long stalk, as in Bird's-foot
Trefoil, but you will see by comparison that the individual
flower is much more slender and pea-like than in that
species.

Bird's-Foot Trefoil.

Yellow Pea.

We are too late to find two other representatives of the family that grow in the fields hereabout. One is the Yellow Vetchling (*Lathyrus aphaca*), which bears its pale yellow flowers solitarily on a long stalk. We should like to have shown this to you, because it is far from common, but chiefly because the whole of its leaf has been converted into

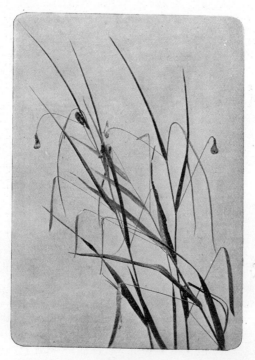

Grass Pea.

tendrils, and the functions of the leaves have to be performed entirely by the stipules, which are developed to a very large size for the purpose.

The other species was the more plentiful, but equally interesting, Grass Pea (*Lathyrus nissolia*), which has no leaves either, but its leaf-stalk is flattened out in the shape of a grass-blade. And this is not because the leaf has been converted into tendrils, for it has none; neither has it any stipules worth mentioning, for these are reduced to mere bristles. Here are a few plants with their straight pods, for the flowers are all over. If we had come along here, say in April, and had then set you to find some plants of the pea tribe on this spot, you would have failed in all probability to separate them from the grasses among which they grow, so like are they to the real thing. But in June you would have identified them by means of their solitary crimson flowers. And now that they are in fruit they are almost invisible again, for their pods are flattened from the sides and look like turned-down grass-blades. So that, you see, even in a small genus where the flowers are so uniform in character, one may find great diversity in the general form and appearance.

So much for the wild peas of the field. Now we must hark back to the Umbellifers, for here is another big fellow demanding attention. He is not so big and spreading as the Cow Parsnip, but he is equally tall. This is the Wild Parsnip (*Peucedanum sativum*)—not a Parsnip by courtesy like the Hogweed, for *Peucedanum sativum* is the real Simon Pure from which those fat sugary tap-roots of the kitchen garden have been evolved by the skill of the cultivator. It has fine ornamental leaves of the pinnate type —that is to say, there are many oval leaflets on opposite sides of the midrib which is terminated by an odd three-lobed leaflet. But the leaves in this species stand almost erect, and are glossy, as compared with the spreading, rough leaves of Cow Parsnip. When the stem has attained the height of four or five feet—sometimes before—it spreads out its flat-topped umbels of small yellow flowers; and these are succeeded by fruits that are not unlike those of Cow Parsnip, but more oblong in shape and smaller. Draw up one of the roots from the ground, and if you expect to find anything like those your well-dug kitchen garden produces you will be disappointed. This is little better than a bit of hard stick. Think what a patient and confident genius was the man who first conceived the idea that cultivation would turn this into a succulent and nutritive vegetable. We can only suppose that primitive man was glad even to gnaw these tough and innutritive sticks, and that the idea occurred to him that if he sowed the seeds in his own plot it would save a good deal of hunting for them. The deeper, lighter soil enabled the plant to feed better, and to store some of its surplus in its tap-root. Our forefather would then immediately see that cultivation paid, for, in addition to having a stock of food close at hand, it was of a quality that reduced the hard labour of eating considerably. And so by persevering he would gradually improve the size, weight, and tenderness of his Parsnips, so that he would take all the prizes at the local shows, if such festivals were known to primitive man. We know that Parsnips must have been cultivated at an early date, for although the Romans had not attained to excellence in their production, they had found out where they could be obtained, for Pliny tells us that the Emperor Tiberius sent every year to the banks of the Rhine for a supply.

There is the Wild Carrot (*Daucus carota*) not far off, and its history as a cultivated vegetable probably runs side by side with that of the Parsnip. Pliny says that in his time the best Carrots came from Candia. The Wild Carrot is not so imposing a plant as the Wild Parsnip, but in a way it is more beautiful. Just glance at the intricate divisions of the compound leaf, as delicate and symmetrical as a fern-frond, but softer in texture than most ferns. It really looks as though some of the ladies in the days of the first Charles had more taste and less barbarism than their modern descendants, for Parkinson tells us that they wore Carrot-leaves instead of feathers. They must have required constant renewal, for the Carrot-leaf soon loses its freshness when detached from the plant.

The Carrot has not a hollow stem like Wild Parsnip and Cow Parsnip; it is solid and furrowed, and clothed with stiff short bristles. The dense compound umbel of white flowers is saucer shaped, and the flowers in the centre of the hollow are pink or purplish. Its oblong fruits have rows of spines down the sides and along the edges.

Another common weed of the field border and all waste places is the Sow-thistle. One should say Sow-thistles, for there is the Common Sow-thistle (*Sonchus oleraceus*) and the Corn Sow-thistle (*Sonchus arvensis*). Those are Sow-thistles of which yonder boy has a goodly bundle under each arm. In all probability he keeps tame rabbits, and there are few things in the way of green-meat a rabbit likes better than Sow-thistles. The rabbit-keeper knows them as "Milkies," which is short for Milk-thistle, an alternative name, indicating that their juice, like that of Lettuce and Dandelion, is white. *Sow*-thistle in this case means that the Porcine tribe are really fond of it. One species at least was formerly a pot-herb in this country, but has been supplanted by cultivated vegetables. The "thistle" portion of its name is not to be taken seriously : it reminds one of Bismarck's summary of one of his contemporaries, that he was "a lath painted to resemble iron." The Sow-thistle is a tender juicy herb, whose thin, brittle leaves are cut up into lobes and teeth that end in spines—but the spines are soft. There is something of a *noli me tangere* look about them, but they lack the toughness and almost shrubbiness of the real Thistle.

This tall plant, something between four and five feet in height, ending in a cluster of large yellow flower-heads, is the Corn Sow-thistle (*Sonchus arvensis*), so-called on account of its liking for corn-fields, where it may frequently be seen over-topping the corn-plants. It has a stout, angled stem, but it is hollow. Its leaves are variable in shape and size, but rather slender, with waved margins decorated with bristles that look like spines, and glaucous on the underside. The upper stem

Wild Parsnip.

leaves half-clasp the stem in the lobes at their base. The flower-heads may be passed by as uninteresting because they are yellow and look at a little distance like Dandelion and Cat's-ear; but looked at more closely they will be seen to have character and beauty of their own. They may be two inches across, and their florets are all strap-shaped, their yellow clear and bright. The involucre is broad and swollen, somewhat after the thistle-fashion, but covered with spreading, knob-tipped glandular hairs.

There is another species here, the Common Sow-thistle (*Sonchus oleraceus*), not so tall, but making up for the deficiency by its branching and greater leafiness. The flowers, too, are only half the size, and even then are proportionately less fine, the heads being crowded into an umbel and not opening so fully. The leaves are more lobed, and in one form (the sub-species *asper*) the margins are all turned up crisply, and the soft spines along the edges are more abundant, so that it looks quite a formidable plant to grasp.

We are in the way of yellow flowers to-day. Here is another one, though its yellow is paler and clearer than what we have been looking at. This is the Yellow Toadflax (*Linaria vulgaris*), and it presents a strong contrast to the little Ivy-leaved Toadflax (*Linaria cymbalaria*) with pale purple flowers, you will remember that we found creeping down the wall in the lane a few months ago—where doubtless we could find it still in flower. This instead of creeping down, stands uprightly, with its stem well clothed with very narrow leaves of a glaucous hue, and ending in a crowded raceme of long-spurred yellow flowers. The flower at once suggests Snapdragon. It has a couple of pouting lips, of which the lower one is greatly swollen and orange-coloured as an indication to bees of the way in. Gently press the sides of the flower and these lips will part, just as they do in the garden Snapdragon, and disclose the stamens and pistil within. The Toadflax is a bee flower, and only

II.—P

such powerful insects can exert sufficient strength to force the lips open. The honey is contained in the long hollow spur, and even the long-tongued bees are not able to reach it without thrusting their heads well into the flower and rubbing their backs against anthers and stigma. Honey-

Goat's-Beard "Puff."

bees and some of the smaller humble-bees have to crawl right in, but some of these show a cuteness that only students of insect life would be likely to credit them with. To save time and trouble they bite a hole in the spur from outside, and so get at the honey without rendering any service to the plant. This, of course, is very reprehensible conduct on the part of the bee, seeing that the flower has specially adapted

Corn Sow-Thistle.

its parts to keep out less important insects. Those of us who live long enough may see some development, in the nature of a reprisal, though we do not quite see how it is to come about, unless the juices of the flower - tissue can be made so objectionable to bee tastes that they will prefer to act honestly rather than bite the flower. That plan has been adopted in innumerable cases by plants to make their leaves and stems unpalatable to herbivorous animals.

Yellow Toadflax is one of the brightest and prettiest of the flowers of late summer and autumn, and as it grows plentifully beside the roads and lanes as well as along field-borders, it is one to be thankful for.

The last Goat's-beard (*Tragopogon pratense*) has flowered, but here is a group of "puffs" which are to distribute the seeds and make provision for next season's display. There is little fear of these being mistaken for the similar globe of fruits of the Dandelion—which is still blooming and seeding around us. The parachute of the Dandelion consists of simple silky .hairs radiating from the beak of the fruit. Here we have a larger fruit with a long beak, from which radiate about a couple of dozen rigid shafts from which stand out on either side a great number of silky filaments which interlace with those of neighbouring shafts. The "puff" is much larger than that of Dandelion, and looks dirty by comparison with the pure white globes of that plant, so that it becomes more easy to find the plant in fruit than when it is in flower. Look at these fruiting heads that have not yet expanded their "puffs," and you will see the object of the long involucral bracts that appeared so ridiculous in proportion to the small flowers. When the flower-heads closed up these bracts came together, and formed this huge beak within which the fruits matured. Now they part a little as development proceeds, and disclose a tuft of hair pencils with long handles. The expansion of the fruits causes these pencils to separate widely, and forces the bracts to fall back. And now that there is sufficient room the bristles of each

pencil fall down until they are all radiating from their
support, and thus you have the complete globe formed. Yes,
even the behaviour of the carpels, after the showy parts of
the flower have faded, is a matter of considerable interest,
especially if followed up to the dispersal of the seed and the
action of the seed when it has got fixed in the proper place
for germination.

A Ragwort Colony.

Yellow Toadflax.

Wild Hop—Male Flowers.

On the Pilgrim's Way.

AUGUST ON THE HILLS.

IN August we get the full power of the sun upon us on the hills, and the climb up if taken by a steep incline is likely to be rather fagging; but we will take it gently by a more circuitous route, and after all when we are at the top we are almost certain to encounter a bit of breeze. That, of course, is not good for camera work, but we have had to encounter it before, and though it has caused us many disappointments we have contrived to get some passable results.

Let us take this lane for a start. Many of the flowers we have already had under notice are abundant here. There are several creepers scrambling over the hedges—Wild Clematis, Honeysuckle, the two Bryonies, Bittersweet—ah, and here is another we have not taken special note of, though its vinelike leaves have been covering big spaces on the hedges for some time. There is no need to tell you it is the

Wild Hop (*Humulus lupulus*), for its resemblance to the
cultivated plant is so close that there is no room for doubt.
But when you look at the bines in the Hop-gardens you only
see part of the species, for the Hop is one of the diœcious
plants — that is, plants that are either male *or* female.
Until they flower you cannot distinguish them, but now
they are in full bloom there is no difficulty, and we have
here the two kinds not very far apart. The flowers of the
two sexes are so different in appearance that, seen apart
from the leaves, they might easily be taken to be the
products of entirely distinct species. The pollen is carried
from the male to the female flowers by the intervention of
the wind, and the stigmas are specially fitted for catching
it as it flies. This being the case the plants have no need
to bother about the production of showy corollas for the
attraction of insects to its service; but some plants under
similar conditions do produce corollas though only small
green ones. The Hop is content with sepals only, and in
the male flowers there are five separate ones, enclosing five
stamens. These flowers, which are about a quarter of an
inch across, are clustered in large panicles. Each female
flower consists of a single sepal, enclosing the somewhat
flattened ovary whose upper part bears a pair of long, curved
stigmas which hang outside the flower. The female flowers
are united into heads or cones, which consist of a number of
overlapping tough bracts in each of which are a couple of
flowers. This develops into the familiar yellow " Hops,"
such as are picked from the bines in the Hop-gardens and
go to the breweries after they have been thoroughly dried in
the oast-houses. The importance of the Hop is due to the
secretion of a resinous principle called *lupuline* which is
found deposited in grains upon the scales of the cone.

Here is the cornfield, and it is getting ripe for the reapers.
There are fine heavy ears here, and plenty of Poppies too.
This is the Common or Corn Poppy (*Papaver rhœas*) that
has been painting agricultural lands red during the past two

Wild Hop—Female Flowers.

months. In the latter part of June, when the Poppies were as tall as the Wheat, some of the fields seemed to be full of them, and anyone unaccustomed to the sight might have imagined that Poppies were the main crop that the farmer was setting himself to raise. But now that the ears have shot up above the flaming flowers the effect of the Poppies is somewhat subdued, though they are still there. Here at

Poppies in the Corn.

the very edge of the field we have a good opportunity for observing the flower in all its stages. Here are the plump buds drooping on their bristly stems, and here the two glaucous sepals that will fall off to-morrow are just slightly separated, showing a little of the crumpled silken petals between. Most other unopened flowers have their petals most carefully rolled up, so that there is not a crease; but the bursting Poppy looks as though its petals had been bundled into the sepals in a great hurry, with excessive crumpling as the result. And yet soon after the sepals have fallen away the juices of the flower rush into the four flabby petals, and they expand quite smoothly. See what a crowd the stamens make around the roofed round-house in the centre. That central structure seems intended as an alighting place for the convenience of insect visitors. They can have no difficulty in seeing a Poppy from a distance, and when they have settled upon this platform they are within reach of the entire circle of anthers. It is the vivid colour that attracts them, and probably some of them imagine that such a fine display betokens a liberal supply of honey; but never a drop of nectar does the Poppy provide for the refreshment of its visitors. There is plenty of pollen, however, and bees, flies, and beetles can alike appreciate that, though a ton of it would not appeal to a butterfly or moth. The central roof is the top of the pistil, and those lines that radiate from its centre to the circumference are the stigmas, upon which the pollen-collecting insects are sure to leave a little brought from the last Poppy they visited. As soon as fertilisation has been effected, off drop the petals and the stamens, and the pistil grows into the capsule which, when it has become very large, will be known as the Poppy-head.

There are Poppy-heads here almost full-grown, which were produced by the first flowers that opened, and they are well worth examination. One such contains sufficient seeds to plant a good-sized corner of the field, and the farmer would probably have no objection if we took all his Poppy-heads away; so we need not hesitate to destroy one of them in the pursuit of knowledge. Let us cut this driest-looking one across, and we shall find the interior more or less completely divided into compartments by partitions which have grown out from the outer walls, and upon which the immature round seeds were produced. As these get ripe they become detached, and when the dry Poppy-head is

Weld.

shaken they rattle inside. But they do more. Look here, under the overhanging eaves of the roof are a number of semicircular lobes which turn down a little and leave openings in the walls of the capsule. As the wind swings the heads on their long stalks the small seeds get shaken out of these openings a few at the time, and so the Poppy crop of next year is sown before this year's wheat crop is harvested.

The grasses and other plants are so thick and tall that we are sure to overlook many things that are now in flower; but this spiry Weld (*Reseda luteola*) that grows so tall and straight beside our path is not likely to be passed by unnoticed. It is one of the Mignonette family, and the Wild Mignonette proper (*Reseda lutea*) is not likely to be very far off. There is a clump of it a dozen yards or so ahead. Very closely allied are these two, and yet, until you enter upon a close examination, very different in appearance. For the Weld or Dyer's Weed sends up a slightly branched stem to the height of two or three feet, with slender, lance-shaped leaves and a raceme of small yellow-green flowers that is almost a spike, for the flower-stalks are exceedingly short. The flowers, regarded as individuals, are very similar to those of the garden Mignonette (*Reseda odorata*). There are three or five petals, the upper and side ones cut up into several lobes, the lower undivided; twenty to twenty-four stamens, and several united carpels open at the top. Around the lower part of these carpels there is a disk on which honey is spread for the attraction of insects. The name Dyer's Weed has reference to the fact that a yellow dye is obtained from the plant, and it is the source of the artists' colour known as Dutch Pink.

The other species, Wild Mignonette (*Reseda lutea*), is quite distinct. It is a shorter, more tufted plant, being more branched from the base. The leaves are cut up into a few unequal lobes, the racemes are conical, more densely flowered, the flowers larger and bright yellow. There are six

II.—Q

each of sepals and petals, and from sixteen to twenty stamens. This is a much less common plant than Weld, for whilst that is found in all sorts of districts where there are dry wastes and roadsides the Wild Mignonette is more partial to chalky soils.

Of course, we are on the chalk again now, but soon we must make a descent into the valley on the other side of the hill, for we ought to visit a certain copse beside the stream where there are still a few moisture-loving plants to be found. First, however, look at those masses of gold that splendidly reflect the sunshine in its proper hues. They are patches of Biting Stonecrop (*Sedum acre*) with their five long, pointed petals spread widely and making the conventional star-shape, like "patines of bright gold." Their ten stamens are also yellow. Apart from the flowers, what a quaint little plant it is with its stems first drooping or creeping, then curving up erectly, and crowded with the fat, humpy, egg-shaped leaves. The Sedums are what are known as succulent herbs. They grow in hot dry places, and in their thick-skinned leaves they store up considerable quantities of fluid that enable them to tide over dry periods when other shallow-rooting plants perish. But this very provision against accident exposes them to another danger—that of being eaten by thirsty animals. The Cacti and other succulent plants protect themselves by developing terrible fine-pointed spines that enter the lips and tongues of those beasts that dare to meddle with them. The Biting Stonecrop has not a spine upon it, and appears to be defenceless against the thirsty rabbits that swarm up these hills. So little does the Stonecrop care for this danger that it grows thickly on the light soil scratched out by the rabbits in making their burrows, for it is protected by making its juices acrid, so that they blister the lips of those that essay to crop the stems, and act as an emetic if taken into the stomach.

Just by the rabbit burrow here is a fungus—to be more precise the Lurid Boletus (*Boletus luridus*)—with a short

Wild Mignonette.

aldermanic stem and a rounded cap of velvety brown. The underside of this cap is deep red, of a waxy-looking consistence and pitted with minute holes. The reddish-yellow stem is covered by a raised network of crimson. This is a very different toadstool from those we have found on our previous rambles together. It differs from the ordinary mushroom type in having closely packed tubes instead of "gills" below

Lurid Boletus.

the cap. In these tubes the spores are produced. Look at this well as it stands, and keep your eyes on it whilst we gather it, for we are about to perform a trick of natural magic. Wherever our fingers touch its stem or tubes the yellow or red is instantly changed to indigo-blue! The flesh within is pale yellow. We break it across, and you have only time to get the merest glimpse of the yellow before it turns to blue. Break it yourself, and you will find that you are every bit as clever as we are in performing the trick. Of course you say "It isn't good to eat!" That is just what almost everybody has said, and the toadstool has got the reputation among the authorities for being one of our most poisonous species. Whether this judgment has been founded upon observation of its effects upon experimenters we cannot say, but it is not at all improbable that the colour prejudice has had its influence. Just look at these grooves in the top of the cap, and look at that other that has been more than half eaten. These marks were made by the teeth of rabbits, so it looks as though this Boletus is not poison to the rabbit. We have never experimented with it, but not many years ago an American mycologist reported to Dr. Cooke that he had eaten it and found it not merely non-poisonous but excellent food! It is probable that the evil reputation of many fungi may have no more solid foundation than prejudice. We had been eating the Blusher (*Amanita rubescens*) for years before we realised that some of the authorities had put it on the black list. We still eat and enjoy it.

We have passed the remains of many Orchid flowers, for June is the great month for Orchids; but a few of them are later. Here is a specimen of the Pyramidal Orchis (*Orchis pyramidalis*), and if you let your eye wander over the down you will see a number of its rosy flower-spikes standing up at intervals. The rather squat, broad-based flowery pyramid on the long stalk makes this species very distinct; but if that should not be sufficient for you there are other identification marks in the great width of the lip, which is broader than long, and the very long, curved spur. Additional attractiveness is given to the spike by the bracts at the base of each flower being coloured to harmonise with the blossoms. It is one of the Orchids that have two round tubers at their base. We may frequently find it in company with the later specimens of Fragrant Orchis (*Habenaria conopsea*), which affords a good opportunity for comparing their respective

points. Seen one apart from the other the tyro may have
doubts as to which of the two species he is looking upon, for

Pyramidal Orchis.

there is a certain resemblance in brightness of colour, and
each has a long spur. But the Fragrant Orchis is more
purple than the Pyramidal, its spur very much more slender
and the spike cylindrical. Its tubers, too, are somewhat
flattened and lobed, and its fragrance is stronger and more
agreeable than that of *Orchis pyramidalis.*

Have you noticed how well patronised the flowers of
Thistle and Knapweed are by butterflies? That is no un-
usual circumstance, but to-day in addition to the Red

Admirals and Meadow Browns there is a larger, brighter insect, with pale reddish wings tipped with black on which are several pure white spots. This is the Painted Lady (*Pyrameis cardui*), of which the home-grown broods are often augmented during this month by vast numbers of immigrants from abroad. Not only do they gather on the nectariferous flowers, but they settle on the paths and dusty roads, and bask in the sun until you are very near to them —then they fly off again. We are evidently in the track of a portion of this invading body, for they are all around us. This one we have been stalking with the camera has at length stayed in one place long enough to yield a photo, but as we had to keep at a distance, it will be too small except for use as a lantern-slide. We must try again when one is engrossed in imbibing nectar from the flowers, and get it at short range.

Here is a find in the way of an abnormal specimen. The Common Daisy (*Bellis perennis*) that greets the rambler all the year round, holding up its bright face in field and lane, by the stream and wood, or on the hills. We photographed it, you remember, quite early in the year ; but this specimen must also have a plate devoted to its beauties, for this is a Daisy of the Progressive sort—a Daisy that is trying to strike out a new line, perhaps ambitious of founding a new

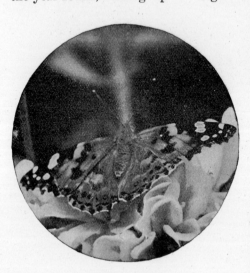

Painted Lady.

Biting Stonecrop.

race. But the idea is not entirely original, for a similar departure has been made before by one of its ancestors, with the result that man captured it and made its descendants into garden flowers. You see what has happened? Instead of a single row of flat white rays to act as advertisements to the tubular yellow florets of the centre, nearly the whole head has been developed into white rays. Right in the centre there are less than a dozen of the tubular florets left, as

"Double" Daisy.

though the plant were anxious to retain some evidence of ancestry. It is what a gardener would call *flore pleno*, though it differs from his own "double" Daisies in the heads being less crowded with florets, and to our mind being consequently more graceful. No; we will not dig up the root and transfer it to the garden. Let us give Nature a chance of working out her own new departures. Leave it under the conditions which produced it, and from time to time when we come this way we may note what happens to the Daisies hereabout. At first sight all these rays appear to be barren—they are evidently rays and nothing else; but if you lift some of them and peer at those below you will see that, like the rays of ordinary Daisies, they have pistils, and consequently the power of reproducing their kind.

It is by seizing hold of chance natural variations of this kind, and breeding from them, that florists have produced so many of our garden flowers, and the old-fashioned red and white Double Daisies probably originated in just such a specimen as we have here.

Let us wade through that breast-deep sea of Ragwort rippling with gold, and make for the belt of Beeches on the farther side of the chalk-pit. The branches are all heavy with the prickly nuts, or "mast," which have now reached full-size—a clear reminder that autumn is on the way. The seeds within are as yet little more than empty skins, but another month or so will fill them out. The growth of the Hazel-nut follows similar stages: the shell is completed and hardened whilst as yet the kernel is scarcely discoverable. The ignorant Cockney comes out, and is delighted to find nuts before they have been on sale in the shops. Instead of cracking a few to find out their internal condition, he fills his pockets with them and retires to a shady bank to enjoy himself with a feast of nuts. The yokel whom he despises could have told him there is no use in cracking nuts until September or October. The yokel remembers these things from year to year; the townsman will have forgotten by next August and will go through the performance again.

Here under the Beeches is another Orchid, and we are only just in time for it, and should have found it more abundant last month. It is the Bird's-nest Orchis (*Neottia nidus-avis*), a plant evidently named in the days when people under the influence of the Doctrine of Signatures were always looking out for signs and resemblances among plants to other things. This Orchis, instead of the round or flattened tubers we have found in other species, has for roots a tangled

Bird's-Nest Orchis.

mass of fleshy fibres which were thought to resemble the nest of a bird. The name is not nearly so happy a selection as in the cases of the Bee, the Fly, and the Butterfly Orchids, but as a name of some sort is a great convenience we will not quarrel with it. Just observe that there are no leaves, nor anything green about the plant. Its appearance is much like that of the Broomrapes we found a few weeks ago—a thick fleshy stem almost covered with large flowers, and a few

In the Chalk-Pit.

withered-looking scales below. The whole plant is yellowish-brown in colour. But it is not to be classed with Broomrape ethically any more than botanically. It is a plant that might plead it is "too proud to work, ashamed to beg, too honest to steal." It has given up manufacturing its materials from the earth and air, so has ceased to produce leaves which are necessary in that process. It does not, like Broomrape, stoop to the low artifice of tapping the roots of honest green plants and stealing from them the results of their industry. So it lives upon the discarded substances that the industrious and

II.—R

wealthy plants throw away. It assumes the *rôle* of Lazarus at the gate of Dives. Every autumn the opulent Beeches cast away tons of leaves that have served their purpose and are no longer of use to the trees. There they lie in deep beds in the Beech-woods, and upon this pabulum the Bird's-nest Orchis feeds, just as though it were a fungus. Instead of making new material from the elements, it takes these worn-out leaves, and breaking them up builds a sort of shoddy structure of them. But for the necessity that is laid upon all creatures, plant and animal alike, to perpetuate their species, it is probable that the Bird's-nest Orchis would not take the trouble to produce flowers and seeds. Look at its colour again. Does it not remind you of those loafing, weather-stained tramps, the "snappers up of unconsidered trifles"?

And now out upon the other side of the Beech-wood we are on an "outlier" of gravel, with a change in the vegetation. Heather and Bracken grow upon chalk it is true, but they prefer sandy or gravelly soils, and here they are showing that preference by growing on this side of the wood and not upon that we have left. Come quietly here, for unless we are deceived by appearances in the wrong way, there is something of interest a little ahead. Some time ago, we came across the eggs of the Nightjar, and here is probably one of the results of leaving those eggs undisturbed. Yes! there crouching among the Heather and Bracken is a young Nightjar in a very favourable position for seeing it. Do not go too near or move unnecessarily, and it may imagine it is not seen. All things that are blessed with protective coloration appear to have a knowledge of the fact and to put faith in their comparative invisibility. They consequently make good subjects for the photographer. We once ran down one of the species, and wishing to photograph it in its natural position on a tree—that is with its body *along* not across the limb, as with most birds—we placed it on an oak branch with the photographer's customary "Now, just as you are for

Hemlock.

one moment, please," and the bird appeared to enter into the spirit of the thing. Anyhow, we got our portrait of it without the slightest restraint upon the bird's liberty, just as we have secured one of the present obliging individual. Now, just notice how finely the details of Bracken and Heather and twigs are reproduced in the browns and greys and yellows of its plumage. We have pointed out a sitting bird among the Heather only a few feet away, and our companion

Young Nightjar among Heather.

has failed to distinguish it from its surroundings. We have seen a flushed bird take a low flight for about a dozen yards, then drop with one wing extended and resting across the tops of Bracken, and in an instant it had become a part of the Bracken. It is a wonderful bird, and we have devoted many an evening on the heaths and hills to observing it, as it flies round the Oaks, filling its bearded mouth with the cockchafers and moths that are also on the wing. You may always know when it is occupied in such beneficent work by the weird churring notes that issue loudly from its throat and sound far in the stillness of even.

Those Umbelliferous plants that stand alongside the copse, rearing their flat spreading heads of pure white flowers to a height of five feet, are plainly distinguishable at a distance from Cow Parsnip, that is still abundant in the fields and wastes. If it were May or June you might be forgiven for supposing them to be Beaked Parsley, but the flowering of that has long been over. This is the dreaded Hemlock (*Conium maculatum*), which is believed to have been the state poison of ancient Athens, administered to criminals and other persons whose continued existence was considered to be undesirable. Socrates, you will remember, was one of the distinguished persons to whom an extract of the plant was given. Many modern cases are on record of the fatal mistake made in assuming this plant to be Parsnip, but one is inclined to say with regard to these that such lamentable and culpable ignorance deserved a drastic punishment. No man has any right to remain so utterly ignorant as this, for there is no more resemblance between the two plants than subsists between a pig and an elephant. Possibly this may be one of Nature's methods for the extermination of the "unfit." Hemlock has a smooth furrowed stem, spotted with dull purple, and clothed at intervals with large wedge-shaped, fern-like leaves which are divided into soft leaflets of similar shape, and these again are broken up into fine divisions. These are nothing like the bold and rather coarse pinnate leaves of the Parsnip; and the flowers instead of being yellow are pure white. The plant has a mousy odour, which becomes positively nauseous when the leaves or stems are bruised, instead of the pleasant aroma of Parsnips and many other Umbellifers. The small umbels have at their base three small one-sided bracts, and about ten of these umbels unite to make up the compound umbel, whose bracts vary from three to seven and are symmetrically arranged. The absence of a pleasant aroma is also observ-

Devil's-Bit Scabious.

Scaly Spleenwort.

able in the seeds, which are without the oil-tubes noticed in Hogweed.

The sloping pasture over which we are now walking contains an abundance of a flower that will be about for the next two months. There is so much of it that it looks as though the farmer had sown it as a crop. But no one is likely to have taken trouble to sow the Devil's-bit Scabious (*Scabiosa succisa*) for it is planted generously enough by Nature, and as it has a perennial root-stock it comes up in the same places year after year without need of renewal. It is one of the Teasel family, but its small dark-blue flowers, gathered into globular heads an inch or more in diameter, might lead one to suppose it belonged to the Composite family. These heads are on very long stalks, which oscillate merrily in the breeze, and reduce the question of getting a successful photograph to a matter of pure chance. The individual flowers of which the head is composed, you will find to be tubular and curved with four lobes round the mouth, and four stamens projecting from it. Here and there we can see a white head among the blue, but this is an exceptional vagary. The plant is between two and three feet high, and its leaves are oblong; those from the root stalked, but not those from the stem. We suppose that most persons know that its peculiar name is due to the sudden way in which its root-stock terminates—botanists term it a premorse root—which had to be explained by invoking the aid of the Evil One, and saying that he must have bitten it off and so prevented it from finishing off as roots should. We have elsewhere quoted Culpepper on this point, but as he puts the matter so quaintly we feel we ought to give it again for your benefit. Here it is, taken from his " English Physician enlarged " (1788). " This root was longer, until the devil (as the friars say) bit away the rest of it from spite, envying its usefulness to mankind; for sure he was not troubled with any disease for which it is proper." We suppose the worthy " Nich. Culpepper, gent."

has good authority for his statement as to the other Nick's immunity from the long list of ailments for which this Scabious is "medicinable," but it seems a pity that he should escape them all. The full list is too long to quote, but among other things "The herb or root (all that the devil hath left of it) being boiled in wine, and drank, is very powerful against the plague and all pestilential diseases or fevers, poisons also, and the bitings of venomous beasts."

We are in the lane now, and there is a rough wall here that will be worth our while looking at. Such structures— if respectably old and not kept in too good a state of repair —are always worthy of attention from the naturalist. Its base bulges in parts, and is well draped with mosses and many other plants. What we specially seek just now is a fern that is rare in these parts but abundant in some other districts. Here it is—the Scaly Spleenwort or Rustyback (*Asplenium ceterach*). There are very few specimens here, the mere remnants of what was once a prosperous colony, but apparently the collectors in turn all but cleared it out. We will not photograph these, as we have a negative taken where they are at once more abundant and more vigorous.

The Scaly Spleenwort is the most distinct of all our native ferns, and there is no danger when once it has been identified of confusing it with any other species. The single character of the frond being clothed at the back with rust-coloured scales having hair-like teeth is sufficient for that. For the rest, it is a small frond—five or six inches long —with wavy margins. Technically it is pinnatifid—cut into lobes in a pinnate manner but not to the midrib. On the upper side the frond is smooth and firm, rather leathery, of a bright deep-green colour. The wiry stalks of the fronds are also clothed in scales. Looking at the fronds you might imagine that they differ from those of other ferns in bearing no spores; but the clusters of spore-capsules are there in ridges hidden beneath the scales on the back. The Scaly Spleenwort is an evergreen, and although its natural habitat

Crooked Yellow Stonecrop.

must be on rocks, where it is found occasionally, you will usually find it on old walls. In some parts of Ireland it is exceedingly plentiful—in County Kilkenny, for example, where we have found it almost the commonest weed, covering great stretches of roughly-built, low boundary walls. In continued dry weather the frond shrivels and curls up, but this is evidently only a provision against excessive evaporation from the naked surface, for after a good shower of rain it will unroll again and present a fresh appearance.

This large Sedum that is crowding over part of the wall, is more plentiful at its foot, and has even climbed into the thatch of the neighbouring cottage, was probably once planted in the garden. It is the Crooked Yellow Stonecrop (*Sedum reflexum*), and considered to be a native in two or three of its haunts ; but in most places a garden escape, that has established itself in a wild condition. We know some lanes where it covers considerable spaces on the hedge-banks. The Sedums are very difficult to kill, and the collector often resorts to boiling water to make sure that the specimens he is pressing for his herbarium will not send out roots and new shoots in his drying press. So you may be sure that any fragments that get broken off in tidying up a garden and are then thrown out on the rubbish heap are not very likely to die from neglect. Drop such a piece anywhere on the ground and it will soon send out fine pale roots and establish itself. Something of the kind has happened here, but the plant has spread considerably along the lane. It has a perennial root-stock from which it sends off numerous trailing branches, and in spring these burst into shoots which are at first neat little tufts of long, awl-shaped, fleshy leaves which curve upwards. But in summer it sends up a large number of crooked flowering stems whose leaves mostly turn downwards, and the stem ends in a spreading cyme of bright yellow flowers nearly an inch across. See how busy the bees are about the flowers, for they contain plenty of honey. Two bees we noticed were busy extracting the nectar as we exposed our plate, and if they kept their wings and legs quiet for a moment they should reappear in the photo. Our operations have awakened the interest of the urchin who sits basking in the hot sunshine on top of the wall. He evidently thinks we are, like Dr. Syntax, in search of the picturesque, and that we are bound to expose a plate on the thatched cottage; so he has taken up "a coign of vantage" where he will become almost necessarily a part of any view that can be taken of the cottage. Why do children manifest this keen desire to be included in photographs that they will probably never see?

"The Neighbouring Cottage."

Bittersweet Berries.

In the River Meadows.

AUGUST IN THE MEADOWS.

THERE is not much in the Meadows just now that we have not already seen, though many of the plants we met with a month ago are still flowering profusely. The Clovers of several species are again in flower; the White Clover (*Trifolium repens*) is very conspicuous, but this little Hop Medick (*Medicago lupulina*), though it has been with us on many occasions, we have not yet taken particular notice of. It sends out trailing stems from the root-stock to the length of a couple of feet or more, and these are tough, much branched, the branches beginning with a comparatively large, slightly toothed trefoil, and half-heart shaped stipules. The individual flowers are only about an eighth of an inch long, bright yellow, but are gathered into oval heads. These are succeeded by much larger oblong heads of kidney-shaped pods with a coiled tip and covered with a raised network of nerves. Each pod contains one seed only, and when this is ripe the pod turns black. It is called the Hop Medick,

II.—S

because its flower heads have a sort of resemblance to the female catkins of the Hop.

But a better representation of the Hop among Leguminous plants is afforded by the Hop Trefoil (*Trifolium procumbens*), a plant of somewhat similar habit, with downy stems, larger trefoils, and larger heads of yellow flowers. The pods are egg-shaped, and covered by the persistent calyx—a character which serves to distinguish it from the Hop Medick at once. They are both here, and with them the large rosy-purple heads of the Red Clover (*Trifolium pratense*), and the smaller ones of similar colour put up by the Zigzag Clover (*Trifolium medium*).

The golden spikes of Agrimony (*Agrimonia eupatoria*) have now grown very tall, and what were flowers when we photographed it have now turned to the top-shaped little burs that transfer themselves securely to our dress as we pass them. With such an admirable means of dispersing its seeds, there is little fear that the Agrimony will become extinct or even rare.

Butterflies are still plentiful, and to the Meadow-browns and Small Heaths are now added Small Tortoiseshells (*Vanessa urticæ*) and Red Admirals (*Vanessa atalanta*). There are plenty of flowers for their delectation on the Creeping Field Thistles (*Cnicus arvensis*) and the Black Knapweed (*Centaurea nigra*). This common Creeping Thistle is one of the pests of agriculture, and some estimable persons assure us that it was especially designed by a beneficent Creator as a lasting punishment to the agriculturist on account of the shortcomings of the original gardeners. But these genial homilists overlook the fact that this species is not of world-wide occurrence. On the American Continent, for example, it was unknown until introduced in modern times. We have sometimes seen labourers in the fields industriously chopping off the stems of this thistle, with a view to exterminating it; but you might as well try to eradicate the grass on a lawn by mowing it, for the Field

Purple Loosestrife.

Thistle has strong creeping root-stocks deep in the ground, and, as soon as the labourer's back is turned, it begins to send up fresh stems. The Field Thistle is peculiar, in that all the flowers of one patch will be male, whilst all those of another patch will be female, though both patches may be connected with the same underground stem. The female heads are egg-shaped, the males are rounder. It is not so handsome a plant as most of our thistles, the purple of the flowers being dull and the down of the seeds dirty-looking.

Here, against the hedge, is a plant that is probably known by sight to most ramblers at this time of the year, and yet probably of those familiar with it not five per cent. could tell you its name. In such cases the public is a "lumper," but as a rule instead of doing as the botanical lumper does—simply aggregate a number of related forms whose specific identity is not above suspicion—the public lumper brings together plants that have only a superficial resemblance, but which when closely examined are found not even to be closely related. Thus it is that Cat's-ear is classed as a drawn-up specimen of Dandelion, and this Calamint (*Calamintha officinalis*) is thrown in with the Hedge Woundwort (*Stachys sylvatica*) and other Labiate plants with purple flowers.

Calamint is a softly hairy plant with the usual square stem of the Labiates, about three feet high, and with distant opposite egg-shaped leaves which are downy and have rounded saw-like teeth along the margins. The rosy-purple flowers are in stalked cymes, that all turn forward. The ribbed calyx-tube is long, and expands widely to the mouth, where there are five bold teeth ending in fine hair-like points. This Calamint (or Beautiful Mint to give the equivalent of its Greek name) is a wonderful cure-all, according to the old herbalists. If all that Culpepper says of it be true, it should be worth much more than its weight in gold.

Look at this great stretch of hedge, almost covered with Bittersweet (*Solanum dulcamara*). We have met with it many times before, and photographed it when it was in full flower. There are still many flowers upon it, but its chief glory just now are the egg-shaped berries that hang so gracefully in cymes. You can see by one of these how the flowers came out in succession. At one end of the cyme the full-formed berry is a beautiful shining red, the one next to it less red and smaller, and so on to the other side of the cyme where the smallest berry is still green, whilst between it and the red ones you have berries of orange and yellow. This shows that the berries, at first green, as they enlarge become yellow, then orange, and finally red.

Just let your eye wander over the grass and you will notice some rings of various dimensions, marked in brighter green than the surrounding grass can show us yet. They are "fairy rings," similar to those we found on the Downs months ago. Their nature is the same, but they are the product of another species of Mushroom—the Horse Mushroom (*Psalliota arvensis*), the species that is best known to the townsman, because it is the one he obtains from his greengrocer. Here are a few specimens already up and expanded, and if you look among the grass—following the fresher colour of the rings—you will see many of the unexpanded heads just peeping through the soil. If you would like a good dish of mushrooms, come along here early to-morrow morning and you shall find more than you want. Some people affect to despise this mushroom because of its name, which indicates its comparative coarseness, larger size, and stronger flavour, as compared with the cultivated Mushroom (*Psalliota campestris*), but such criticism often falls from lips that have never tasted the smaller kind. *We* think that if you can gather your own Horse Mushrooms, thus making sure that they are fresh, sound, and not maggoty, you are quite as well off as though you had the dung-hill-grown species; but there will never be wanting those who decry that which is produced by Nature in abundance, and acclaim that which is produced in lesser quantity. Country people say *campestris* is better for eating, but *arvensis* better for ketchup.

The Horse Mushroom varies in size when expanded from two to eighteen inches across the cap, which is creamy white, of the texture of kid. The broad gills are at first white or pale flesh tint, gradually darkening with the ripening of the spores until they are dark purple-brown.

Now let us get down the stream, for there is a beautiful plant in flower just now, as you can see from here without mistaking its identity. It is the Purple Loosestrife (*Lythrum salicaria*), a plant that is fond of moisture, and in consequence

Horse Mushroom.

is rarely found away from a stream or ditch. We have found it abundantly growing up seaside cliffs, but, as in the case of the Reed, that was because there was a constant percolation of water through the cliff from the grass lands above. It has a perennial creeping root-stock, from which it sends up several angled stems to a height of three, four, or five feet. Its lance-shaped leaves have a lobed base, and are sometimes in pairs, sometimes in whorls of three or four, and its flowers also are in whorls. This variability in the character of its leaf-bearing is consistent with the general inconsistency of the plant. It has a tubular calyx with twelve ribs and the same number of stamens. There are six narrow, oblong petals of red-purple hue, and they are wrinkled somewhat after the manner of a Poppy's petals. We have called your attention to several plants that have dimorphic flowers, in the sense of variation of length and position of the stamens and style, to facilitate cross-fertilisation, and we have a similar arrangement in *Lythrum*, only it is *tri*-morphic—nay, strictly speaking there are no fewer than six forms giving eighteen different methods of cross-fertilisation. There is a long-styled form, a short-styled form, and a form having a style of medium length; but each of these has two sub-forms, differing in stamens and pollen. That is rather a complicated state of affairs, is not it ? In some localities it has been noted that these different forms of flowers are borne by plants that definitely vary in stature, downiness (or smoothness), and even in the brightness of their flowers, but we are not sure that the differences in the plant are constant.

Here, in the masses of flowers of various kinds that crowd together on the bank of the stream, the Loosestrife is easily the most brilliant. Here are still foam-like plumes of Meadow-sweet, heavily scenting the air, there are the bright yellow clustered and woolly heads of Fleabane (*Pulicaria dysenterica*), and the pale dull-purple masses of Hemp Agrimony (*Eupatorium cannabinum*). Let us take a photo of a small patch that shall include several of these, and show the water rushing by.

The Hemp Agrimony owes its name to the fact that its compound leaves *suggest* the foliage of the Hemp (*Cannabis sativa*) without actually resembling it. One of its claims to our attention lies in the fact that it is the simplest of all our Composite plants. Probably you would not have taken it for a Composite flower at all, for its clusters have a looseness and freedom about them that do not suggest the close packing of the florets such as we find in Daisy, Hawkweed, and Thistle. But all things must have

Hemp Agrimony and Fleabane.

a beginning, and Hemp Agrimony probably represents the primal idea of the composite flower-head, before plants had discovered that greater publicity could be given to minute and inconspicuous flowers by packing several hundreds of them into a small space, so that their united appearance was that of one large and showy blossom.

Now that we have photographed a bit of the mixed mass of riverside flowers, let us focus upon the upper part of a single stem of Hemp Agrimony. At closer quarters you see that the bunches of bloom are made up of smaller bunches, or apparently single flowers; but if you separate one of those apparent flowers you will find it is a head made up of four or five pale reddish-purple florets and invested by a common involucre consisting of about ten overlapping bracts. Each of the florets is essentially the same as a floret from the yellow disk of a Daisy-head—a cylindrical tube with five lobes at its mouth and a similar arrangement of stamens and style, only that the arms of the style are much longer and project far beyond the mouth, causing that fluffiness of the flower-masses. The florets contain honey, and as they are deep and narrow they are favourite refreshment places with the butterflies. There are plenty of them here now, and Peacocks and Admirals are hobnobbing over their cups with Green-veined Whites. The plant was named in honour of Mithridates Eupator, king of Pontus, who is credited with the discovery of its tonic properties. The classical name at some period or other got corrupted into *Hepatorium*, and the herbalists took their cue from this and declared it was a good liver medicine.

That yellow-flowered plant with thick cottony leaves is the Common Fleabane (*Pulicaria dysenterica*), that you may also find growing along ditches and damp roadside wastes. It, also, is a Composite, but it conforms more to the Daisy type, having both tubular disk-florets and ray-florets. It got its name from a belief that if burned its smoke would prove unbearable to fleas who would forthwith

flee from it. Its species name denotes its former use as a
medicine in cases of dysentery.

On one of our June rambles we noticed the Lamb's-
tongue Plantain (*Plantago media*), which was then just
freshly in flower (*see* page 3). Here are other plants of it,
and they are in flower. And right on till October or
November it will still be flowering. The attempt we made
to photograph it on the former occasion was frustrated by
wind-movements at the critical moment of exposure; but
in this corner the air is for the time being as still as we
could desire, so we will make another attempt. Ah! there
was no movement that time; and now we have the satisfaction of having added a beautiful but thoroughly detested
weed to our photographic herbarium. It is certain that
many persons will feel in a much better frame of mind for
admiring it in a photograph than when it is adorning (?) their
lawns unbidden.

Among the weeds that like this moist ground down by
the stream is the Welted Thistle (*Carduus crispus*), although
it is by no means restricted to wet ground. You may meet
with it on the untrimmed roadside, on the hedge bank, or
in neglected pastures. It is a very tall, slim plant with a
stem 4 or 5 feet high, scarcely branched in the lower
half, but bristling with fine spines from the leaves being
continued as wings far down the stem. This gives it the
appearance that has suggested the name Welted—that of
long fillets having been sewn on. These wings are little
more than fringes of spines like very fine needles. The long
slender leaves from the lower part of the stem also end in
long spiny points, and their pinnate lobes are *pin*-nate in
a sense that the makers of botanical terms never dreamt of.
There is, in truth, scarcely space on any part of the plant
where we could grasp it between two finger-tips without
getting those fingers stabbed. The branches are almost erect
and end in a crowded cluster of egg-shaped flower-heads,
from which the purple flowers spread out in graceful curves.

Hemp Agrimony.

The scales of the involucre look as though some small spider had been industriously spinning threads to connect them.

Down at the water's edge, or rather in the water, there is a plant very like the Branched Bur-reed (*Sparganium ramosum*) we photographed the other day. It is indeed the next member of the same genus, the Unbranched Bur-reed (*Sparganium simplex*), a plant you might have some difficulty in deciding as to its distinctness if it were not in flower. It is only about half the height of the other, and its flowering stems instead of being branched and zig-zag are straight and without branches, whilst the heads of male flowers are yellow instead of olive-brown and the female heads are stalked.

Here must end our ramble for to-day. We ought really to have gone out to the heath, for we wanted to show you a beautiful flower that should be out now in moist places, though we fear there is little else there just now beyond what we have already seen. We can at least show you a photograph of the plant to which we refer. Here it is; and its name is the Marsh Gentian (*Gentiana pneumonanthe*). It is a beautiful flower, but by no means a conspicuous one, for it does not open very widely. All the Gentian family are beautiful and neat. This one has rather weak stems, that lean upon the ground for a while, then grow upwards. Its few leaves are very slender, and each shoot or branch ends in a comparatively large flower, that is something between bell-shaped and funnel-shaped. The mouth suggests a bell, but as it is erect and tapers to its base it suggests more of the funnel-shape. Within, it is a beautiful bright dark blue, but its exterior is dull blue with broad streaks of green. You will find it growing among Heath, but it requires a good deal of searching for, and it is very local.

Another plant that we might find in flower just now, if we could take a run down to the coast, is the Sea Holly (*Eryngium maritimum*), but there is so much more to be

done on the hills around here that we must be content to
stay nearer home, although, as the poet sings—

> " Fields wear a wan and sickly hue,
>   And farmers of the drought complain ;
> For rain-streaks on the faded blue
>   Of arching skies, they look in vain :
> Thrice happy now is he who dwells
> Where the great heart of ocean swells "—

and the Sea Holly grows on the dunes.

The Sea Holly is no relation to *the* Holly (*Ilex aquifolium*).
It is really an Umbelliferous plant, allied to Hogweed and
Parsnip, though as unlike these in appearance as possible.
Considering where it grows it ought to be a Cactus, for its
perennial root-stock goes deep into the hot dry sand at the
foot of the cliffs or sandhills where you can scarcely bear
your hand, and it is a marvel that it does not get burnt up.
But its leaves are thick and almost of the texture of card-
board, apparently dry and of a fine glaucous tint with a
" bloom " on it. In spite of its apparent dryness, it is
evidently a tasty morsel, or its margins would not be drawn
out into long spines to ward off any browsing quadruped
ranging the sands for a meal. We may take it, that the
breadth of these leaves also serves the purpose of protecting
the stem and roots from the violent action of the sun that
beats upon them with great power. They are four or five
inches across, and from amid a spreading cluster of them rises
the head of bluish flowers with a suggestion of the Thistle.
Of course, when you look into them, you see that they are
undoubtedly Umbelliferous. The egg - shaped heads are
about an inch across and have a frill of spiny-toothed bracts
for their further protection. It is not a simple matter to
pull one of those heads to pieces, but, if you can manage to
do so, you no longer have doubts as to its family relations.
Each separate flower is only about an eighth of an inch
across with a prickly calyx, and the egg-shaped fruit is also
prickly. The necessity for its protection is made evident

Lamb's Tongue Plantain.

when we find it recorded that formerly the roots were candied and eaten as a sweetmeat. It was also a wonderful medicine of the cure-all kind, and could be drunk as a decoction or used as a plaster. Among the many troubles for which it was prescribed were the king's evil (scrofula), the bitings of serpents, thorns in the flesh, broken bones, imposthumes in the ear, quartan agues, melancholy of the heart, "and also for them that have their necks drawn awry, and cannot turn them without turning their whole body." A wonderful plant!

Close to the Sea Holly, but almost certainly on the landward side of it, we should find a number of other plants, all characterised by their possession of stems and leaves more or less bloated and fleshy. This is a condition apparently induced by growth near the sea. The salt in the air, and the excessive evaporation, seems to necessitate a much thicker cuticle to protect the soft cell tissues within from drying up. It is a modified form of what takes place among the Cacti and similar succulents in Africa, etc., and such as we have seen in our native *Sedums*. Among these plants will be several species of the Goosefoot family (*Chenopodiaceæ*), weeds that come in for very little attention from the average rambler, because they are deficient in the attractions of large or bright coloured flowers. One of these will probably be the Beet (*Beta maritima*) with tall ribbed stems, more or less tinged with red, and large smooth leaves, feeling rather greasy to the touch, that make an admirable substitute for Spinach. There will be Salt-wort (*Salsola kali*) that seems all stem and branches, for its small leaves are awl-shaped, ending in sharp points, and its greenish flowers are solitary and inconspicuous. The Sea Purslane (*Atriplex portulacoides*) will not be far to seek, and it may be known by its lance-shaped succulent leaves being white and hoary as with frost. Its yellow-green little flowers are in long slender spikes. Another species, the Frosted Sea Orache (*Atriplex laciniata*) has its reddish stem as well as its sinuate leaves all covered with the frost-like mealiness.

It is there, too, that we might find the fragrant Chamomile (*Anthemis nobilis*) spreading its stems and finely cut leaves over the sands, and profusely covered with the aromatic flower-heads that might be described as daisy-like but for their conical centres. But no description of the plant is necessary, for anyone who knows the odour of Chamomile will get a strong whiff of it the moment he begins to walk over it.

In such a place, too, one might come upon the Sea-side Bindweed (*Convolvulus soldanella*), with short stems that seldom twine but just lie along the shore, and with large flowers of pink and yellow. But if we go on with the catalogue of sea-side plants you will want to start off at once for the shore, perhaps to be disappointed, for most of the plants that are peculiar to the coast whose flowering time is August are of lowly stature and their flowers small and not superficially striking. So we had better put off that jaunt for a time, and give the woods and hills a turn instead.

Near the Haunt of the Sea Holly.

Welted Thistle.

Marsh Gentian.

The Botanical Bridge.

AUGUST IN THE WOODS

OUR ramble to-day is to be in woods that are mixed, but mainly of Oak. They differ, however, from the Oak-woods we have visited hitherto, in the fact that a beautiful broad salmon river runs through them, and there are varying altitudes from the river level to five or six hundred feet above it. The tree-clad hills condense much moisture from the atmosphere, and this has made channels for itself, so that we shall occasionally come upon cascades and torrents. There is a good private road separated from the river by strips of meadow and osier holts, but above it we shall find only the most delightful of woodmen's paths, and in many cases must make our own track.

We start at the bridge—the bridge that is so covered with vegetation that one could write a considerable chapter on its botany. Not merely is it rich in the ferns and mosses that frequently are portions of picturesque bridges, but numerous larger herbs, shrubs, and even trees are growing from it. It is to be feared that the very beauty of the bridge may some day make it a picturesque ruin. As we stand on it to-day and try to see into the woodland, the river after passing the weir quickly disappears in the mass of foliage that towers far above it. As a matter of fact, the river curves to the left and winds around the wooded hill, on whose top we can just catch sight of the highest branches of that noble grove of Araucarias in the park above; but even its curving is completely hidden by the exuberant foliage, all of the freshest, most vivid green, for we are in the Emerald Isle.

That botanical bridge has a charm for us difficult to resist, but we must get away from it into the meadows under the magnificent Lime (*Tilia platyphyllos*) that towers straight up for eighty or ninety feet. Let us cast a string round it at our chest height and take its girth. Fifteen feet. A fine tree, and we can enjoy just standing and looking up the clean shaft among the branches and watching the varied intensities of the soft green light that comes through the broad leaves. Then on, through the deep grass that is not all grass, for it is liberally mixed with Dog Daisy, Meadow-sweet, and Water Ragwort (*Senecio aquaticus*), the latter resembling the Common Ragwort of dry fields but with much larger flower-heads in more spreading corymbs. There is much to interest us in this meadow, but we must try not to see it, or we shall never get into the woods.

Ah! do you smell anything peculiar? We must take a look at that dead tree whence the odour proceeds. The bark is loose, and as we pull off pieces of it the source of the fragrance is revealed. Huge caterpillars, three and four inches long and as thick as one's finger, are under the bark, or emerging from tunnels in the timber. They have cream-coloured sides, dark red backs, and black heads with power-ful jaws. They are the caterpillars of the Goat-moth (*Cossus ligniperda*), so-called because the abundant odour given off

Water Ragwort.

Sea Holly.

by the caterpillar is supposed to resemble the fragrance of the billy - goat. These caterpillars get into diseased trees, and for several years feed on the wood. It has been stated that they will at once leave a tree that is dead; but this before us is certainly a dead tree, or part of a tree, for only the bole is left, and there are indications that the wood was dead before these caterpillars began their labours upon its demolition. Certainly there is no suspicion of vegetable life in it now,

Goat-Moth Caterpillar.

but there are more caterpillars than we have ever seen of this species before. The caterpillar has rather a peculiar appearance, due to the fact that its mouth and cutting jaws are in front of its head, whereas the usual position among caterpillars of other species is beneath the head. The difference is due to the habits of the insect: as it is always engaged in boring a tunnel, the frontal position for the jaws is a great convenience. It has a peculiar trick of ejecting a fluid from its mouth which gives off the offensive odour, and it has been supposed that it does this to drive away enemies; but we suspect that it is a fluid that has a disintegrating effect upon the woody tissues, and lightens the insect's labour. Will some chemist kindly investigate this point, and tell us what is the chemical nature and property of the fluid?

The caterpillar ultimately becomes the Goat - Moth, a large insect with a wing expansion of over three inches, and mottled with brown and grey, and streaked transversely with darker lines, that enable it to sit on a tree trunk and be almost invisible.

We are on the river walk at last, a beautiful tree-shaded

road with continual glimpses of water on the left, and on the right high rocky banks clad with thick vegetation, among which ferns and mosses are conspicuous. Here is a recess in the bank, evidently water-worn, for the ferns, mosses, grasses, and Golden Saxifrage (*Chrysosplenium alternifolium*) with which it is clothed are all running with water, which collects in a rocky basin below. The excess runs below the road, which has a low mossy stone wall on the riverside to save it

The Weir.

from sliding down; and this wall would delight the fern collector, for it is covered with beautiful tufts of Scaly Spleenwort (*Asplenium ceterach*), which indeed is one of the most plentiful weeds hereabout. One would imagine that ferns, like potentates, agreed to the partition of districts as "spheres of influence," for you may traverse a road for a mile or two and find the Scaly Spleenwort in almost sole possession of the rough stone boundary walls and hedges. Then you find it gives place to the Maidenhair Spleenwort

Maidenhair Spleenwort.

(*Asplenium trichomanes*), or the Black Spleenwort (*Asplenium adiantum-nigrum*). Here you have not to look for ferns—they are in such numbers that they force themselves upon your attention, and the collector may here take sufficient to satisfy him without leaving an appreciable gap. It is a joy to one who has seen the country round London practically denuded of ferns, to know that there are still districts farther afield where the greed of the collector and

Scaly Spleenwort.

the commercial spirit combined have not been allowed to interfere with the continued existence of such beautiful forms of vegetation.

Here they are, all along this woodland road in great variety. At the lower levels there are enormous clumps of Hart's-tongue (*Scolopendium vulgare*), not the short, narrow-fronded type one finds in some localities, but bright-green yard-long fronds two and a half inches broad. Oh, no! neither they nor anything else has been planted here. The

II.— U

road has been made for a certain distance through the wood, but the only landscape gardener who has been allowed to beautify it is Nature herself; and the road is so beautiful that it is impossible to make haste along it. Now and then we come across a recess where probably stone has been dug to repair the road, but if so Nature has been quick to heal the wound—the scars of course remain, but they are covered with the most graceful growths of Hard Fern (*Lomaria spicant*), the barren fronds arching outward, the long slender fertile fronds standing erect above them. What would not one give to have such a recess in one's garden; but it could scarcely be made unless the garden was a piece carved out of a primeval woodland like this.

Now we are out on the open again; a sloping expanse, covered principally with Meadow-sweet and backed by the woods, runs down to the water-side with a fine view down the river on which a great flock of Black-headed Gulls (*Larus ridibundus*) are screaming, and doubtless destroying the Salmon fry. Immediately facing us on the opposite side of the river the bank runs up steeply to a great height completely covered by trees. Our attention is directed that way by the sound of falling water, and we see a column of silver falling straight from half-way up the hill, then striking on the rocks half-way down to the river level, and completing the journey in several cascades. We are going to photograph it, though at this distance, right across the river, the detail must come very small; but the air is clear.

A little farther along the road we come to a round tower, evidently an old fort that protected the demesne against hostile neighbours from adjacent castles who might come up the river and land just below. But its interest to us is not archæological but botanical. From base to summit it is clad in vivid green mosses, and from amid these grow out hundreds of thousand of plants of the Maidenhair Spleenwort Fern (*Asplenium trichomanes*). It is another of the common mural ferns of the district, and is very widely distributed

Angelica.

beyond it; but we have never seen so vast an assemblage at one time. How often in our rambles that passage of Ruskin's—" covering with strange and tender honour the scarred disgrace of ruin "—recurs to us; but here the words have a special application. The fort is a memorial of disgraceful days when war was rife in the land, but Nature has done her best to take away the grim aspect of the tower, and if possible to make men forget the old animosities which such erections keep alive, by making them ad-

Hard Fern.

mire its present peaceful beauty. The crowns are all matted and mixed, and the fronds so cross each other that it would be difficult to get a single plant out of the mass without spoiling its fronds and those of its neighbours. So, if you are

wanting specimens you had better wait until we come upon
an ordinary wall from which we may select separate individuals.   That is the plan we shall adopt with the camera,
for there is far too much of it here to show distinctness.

The Maidenhair Spleenwort (*Asplenium trichomanes*),
called by old Parkinson "English Maidenhair," is a slightly
creeping fern, that gets its roots between the joints of the
masonry, and if growing on the level throws out its tufts of
fronds in circular fashion.   But usually it springs from the
face of the wall, and this character is partially hidden.   Then
the front fronds arch forward or hang downwards, whilst
the back fronds erect themselves against the wall and curve
to one side.   Each frond consists of a wiry dark-brown
channeled midrib, from six to twelve inches in length,
bearing thirty or forty pairs of oblong leaflets (*pinnæ*), a
quarter of an inch long and with the faintest possible suggestion of a footstalk.   On the back these pinnæ are covered
with thick clusters of the brown spore cases, each containing
the innumerable microscopic atoms from which new generations of this fern will be produced.   The pinnæ are jointed
to the midrib (*rachis*), and when they have done all the
work they are capable of and their cells get congested they
appear to be thrown off, for you will find many bare mid-
ribs from which they have all dropped.   The plant had
formerly a great medicinal reputation for many complaints,
and, of course, having the name Maidenhair, and hair-like
stalks, it was considered an admirable corrective for a thin-
ness or absence of the natural head-covering.   Village
herbalists still prescribe an infusion or "tea" of it in cases
of coughs and colds.

The road here runs across a low-walled moss-grown
bridge which spans the lower part of a torrent that comes
down through the woods from the mountain behind.   A
rough road that torrent would make if it were dry, cumbered
as it is with boulders large and small and tree trunks that
have fallen in some storm and been swept down by the

rushing waters, until they have become wedged between the boulders; then the boughs and leaves and other débris have completed a dam over which the waters now pour in flashing cascades. Ferns are everywhere about it on the boulders, or the banks of its sinuous channel. What a collection of mosses and liverworts could be made here, if one had time for it. There, too, is the big Irish Spurge (*Euphorbia hiberna*) that the salmon-poachers are said to use for the purpose of poisoning the rivers, that the salmon may float helpless on the surface. And here is that fine Umbellifer, the Angelica (*Angelica sylvestris*). We are far too late for the flowers of the Spurge, but the Angelica's umbels are only now spreading themselves, and we must get a photograph of it.

The Angelica is one of our largest Umbellifers, with fine handsome shin-

The Waterfall.

ing leaves, whose compound leaflets remind one of the leaves of the Dahlia. Each leaflet is large enough

and sufficiently divided to be reckoned as a large leaf.
Where the leaf-stalk springs from the stem it is expanded
into a large sheath, as in the Cow Parsnip; and also, like that
plant, the tall stout stem is hollow. The great compound
umbel is at first wrapped in broad hollow sheaths, the bases
of bracts which end in a futile effort to be leafy. The rays
from the compound umbel are both numerous and stout,
and the white flowers are nearly regular. You ask why it
should have such a name? Do its virtues so transcend those
of other plants as to deserve such distinction, or is there any
legend to connect it with the angels? Hear, then, what our
old Herbalist says on this point, for it is better than any
explanation we could give :—

"In time of Heathenism, when men had found out any
excellent herb, they dedicated it to their Gods; as the
Bay-tree to Apollo, the Oak to Jupiter, the Vine to Bacchus,
the Poplar to Hercules. These the Papists following, as the
Patriarchs, they dedicate to their Saints—as our Lady's Thistle
to the Blessed Virgin, St. John's Wort to St. John, and
another Wort to St. Peter, etc. Our physicians must imitate
like apes, though they cannot come off half so cleverly, for
they blasphemously call Phansies or Heart's-ease *an herb of
the Trinity*, because it is of three colours: And a certain
ointment, *an ointment of the Apostles*, because it consists of
twelve ingredients: Alas, I am sorry for their folly, and
grieved at their blasphemy : God send them wisdom the rest
of their age for they have their share of ignorance already.
Oh! Why must ours be blasphemous, because the Heathens
and Papists were idolatrous? Certainly they have read so
much in old rusty authors, that they have lost all their
divinity; for unless it were among the Ranters, I never read
or heard of such blasphemy. The Heathens and Papists were
bad and ours worse; the Papists giving idolatrous names to
herbs for their virtue's sake, not for their fair looks; and
therefore some call this an herb of the *Holy Ghost*; others
more moderate call it Angelica, because of its angelical

Tunbridge Filmy Fern.

virtues, and that name it retains still, and all nations follow it so near as their dialect will permit."

We step and leap from tree-trunk to boulder, and creep along the rock-ledges at the sides, occasionally getting a leg or a foot into the water, from attempting a foothold on slippery moss or a rotten bough. But now we have reached firmer ground, though it is very narrow. The trees have grown very tall here, and they are close together. Their canopy shuts out all direct light, and all we get is of a green hue from having passed through the leaves. This is just the light that many ferns like, and they also love the humid atmosphere that is retained by such a canopy over the splashing water. And there are ferns all around, springing from the mosses and the decaying leaves and tree trunks, claiming our attention. They shall get it presently, but, for the moment, we are on a hot scent, for we see at a little distance up the broken overhanging bank a plant that seems something between a moss and a fern. We are almost afraid to give expression to our suspicion of what it may be, but this particle on a bared tree-root that projects from the bank reassures us. It *is* the Tunbridge Filmy-fern (*Hymeno-phyllum tunbridgense*). Going forward we find the lower part of a tree-bole and its thick spreading root-branches thickly coated with a continuous sheet of it. We photograph it, and surely few photographs of a small subject have been taken under greater difficulty. We are not speaking of danger, for the danger was chiefly to the camera; to our person the worst that was likely to happen was a nasty fall, and a tumbling about among the boulders as the torrent swept us down. That has not happened; but it was difficult to get firm foothold for the camera or ourselves on the mossy and loose rocks, all reeking with water. But the real difficulty was, whilst maintaining the camera steady, to get sufficient light, or to accurately judge the exposure needed. For it is clear to see that under this dense leafy roof there is the very smallest actinic value in the light. One might as well be in some heavy-pillared cathedral where every particle of light had to come through stained glass. And then, apart from the light, our subject is so dull and dark. Well, the exposure is made, but we feel sure our difficulties with that plate are not yet over; they will begin again in the dark room.

The Tunbridge Filmy-fern is different from all the Ferns we have hitherto come across. It is well-named Filmy-fern, for the substance of its tiny fronds is so thin that you can almost see through it; and there is no doubt that if the atmospheric conditions of this torrent bed were not similar to those of a closed greenhouse, the fern could not exist here. The root-stock of this species takes the form of a fine creeping wire from which fronds are given off at frequent intervals, but the root-stocks so cross and interlace that the fronds from one get much mixed with those of its neighbours, and the result is a matted sheet extending continuously over all the irregularities of the surface it is clothing. The most prominent thing about the frond is the midrib and its branches, which are so much thicker than the cellular substance of the frond that this appears to consist merely of the ribs and a narrow wing of tissue. As a fact this membrane consists of only one layer of cells, and it has none of the *stomata*, or breathing pores, such as are plentiful in other ferns and flowering plants.

We have already called attention to the way in which the spore capsules are heaped in ridges or clusters on the back of the fronds of Ferns, but here we have quite a different method of spore-bearing. At the base of the pinnæ you will find very minute little urns, something between round and egg-shaped, open at the top, and the mouth with a jagged edge. Within the urn there is a central pillar around which the spore-cases are attached spirally.

After moving our camera into a position of safety, and looking around, we find that every dark cavity under the bank, every fallen trunk, nearly every stone is coated with this delicate fern, which is doubtless one of the oldest

Royal Fern.

inhabitants, though we are sure our kind host to whom we are indebted for the privilege of exploring the deep recesses of this wood, has no suspicion that he has such a treasure on his estate.

Higher up the torrent we push our way through the tangled herbage and over all sorts of impediments. It is warm work, and the hot moist air seems to penetrate our clothing as it does in the Aroid House at Kew. Kew! Ah, what would not our friends there give if they could construct a department like this in the beautiful gardens, but such a torrent and its surroundings is scarcely to be made—it must grow! Why, everyone of those round-topped masses of stone, around which the waters rush and foam, is a thing of beauty, coated with the most delicate gems of moss and crystal-wort and seedling-fern, sparkling with the globules of spray that have been thrown upon them by the swirling waters that

The Torrent

vainly strive to sweep the boulder away. Here and there a
boulder supports a full-grown fern—a Prickly-toothed Buckler
(*Nephrodium spinulosum*), or a Soft-Prickly Shield-fern
(*Aspidium aculeatum*), or even a small tree, such as a graceful Mountain Ash (*Pyrus aucuparia*).

At last we reach what for a moment we think is the top
—it is certainly a level space, and we come upon a cluster of
Strawberry-trees (*Arbutus unedo*). Dare we consider that
these are Nature-planted? The authorities declare that its
only native places are at Killarney, Muckross, and Bantry;
but this is hardly the situation for planted specimens, and
there are no signs that planting has gone on. We are
fortunate to find the tree in flower so early; and it has been
out some time, for there are numbers of the creamy-white
bells lying on the ground, having been cast off when fertilisation was complete. And, hanging from the drooping twigs,
there are many of the rough round fruits formed last year
and now approaching to their full size, for the tree-straw-
berry is a fruit that takes more than a year to swell and
ripen. At the present time they are two or three months
short of that condition, so you cannot test the truthfulness
of the ancients who said that to eat one was enough to
satisfy the eater.

Woodmen are hereabout clearing away some of the too
abundant trees, and we find that what we thought was the
top is only a boggy plateau where we have to walk with
circumspection. A still higher section of the torrent rises
before us, and we dimly perceive, through the dense wood,
that beyond rises Mount Alto, whence the water comes. It
passes here under a low mossy culvert, and we soon give up
its further exploration, attracted to one side over the boggy
ground by the vision of tall ferns and broad, eight or ten feet
high, whose identity there is no mistaking. It is the Royal
Fern, the *Osmunda regalis*, not in the position we should
like, for those that we dare come near enough to are tangled
up with undergrowth, and those that are more free are on

II. *Pl.* 77.

Male Fern.

X 154.

ground so soft and spongy that probably both camera and photographer would be lost to sight for ever. For the same reason it is not possible to so fully clear away obstructions in the foreground as usual. We make several essays to approach, but the ominous trembling and heaving of the surface sends us back again to the rocks by the cascades, from which position of safety we can enjoy a view of the surroundings. Royal Fern is a prominent ingredient of the undergrowth, and some of the plants are doubtless of great age, for their root-stocks form considerable hillocks, more than two feet high, which have divided into a score or more of crowns. The enormous fronds are quite distinct in appearance—apart from size—from our other Ferns, for their rich green leafy portions are of a thick leathery consistence, and the stalk (*stipes*), is free from the clothing of chaffy scales. The frond is divided into a number of huge *pinnæ*, each large enough to be regarded as a full-sized fern-frond, and subdivided into large flat oblong pinnules. In some of the fronds the leafy portion of the pinnules is greatly reduced or contracted, and densely coated with red-brown spore-capsules. Superficially observant persons in the past, who noted this distinct manner of spore-bearing, saw a resemblance to the clustered small red flowers of Dock and Sorrel, so assumed that these also were flowers, and christened the Royal Fern the Flowering Fern. Such a name is a flat contradiction, for no fern, as such, produces anything analogous to a flower—though the intermediate plant which arises from the germination of a spore possesses sexual organs by which a new frond is finally produced.

At one time the Royal Fern must have been very abundant in these islands, and there is still a good deal of it left here in Ireland, in Wales, and Cornwall; but as recently as thirty years or so ago it was plentiful in some of the Surrey valleys, where the only reminder of it to-day is a stray specimen growing in the garden of a keeper's cottage. The others have been chopped into small crowns, the fibrous roots all cleared off, and the dry remains sold by the dealer as Flowering Ferns. The unsophisticated purchaser has planted these in the dry forecourts of Suburbia where, after unfolding their existing frond-buds and vainly endeavouring to put out sufficient new root-fibres to support them, they have died after a season or two. It would be interesting to have a return of the hundreds of thousands of choice ferns that were sacrificed during one decade—say 1875 to 1885— to the uninstructed enthusiasm for fern-growing that then raged.

There is a much more delightful method of fern-growing which we have always inculcated—a method that does not detract from the natural beauty of the woods and valleys, but which is not in harmony with the modern " raw haste " to attain results without trouble. It consists in the collection of a fertile frond of several species of fern, shaking out the spores over suitable soil in seed pans, covering with glass, and watching the development of the *prothalli* and the subsequent seedling-ferns. Such ferns will be finer than the half-dead specimens purchased from the dealers, and there will be the satisfaction of knowing that our possession of them has not deprived any other Nature-lover of the full enjoyment of their native haunts.

We rather unwillingly turn our backs upon the torrent and the dense woods, and make our return to the riverside by a shaded path that leads down a picturesque glen, where the rocks that crop out on either side and the high mossy banks are well clothed with ferns of several species. There is not time to take particular note of all, but we must glance at a few of them in passing.

Of course, there is the Male-fern (*Nephrodium filix-mas*) which is ubiquitous wherever ferns will grow, and which stands boldly like a large green shuttlecock on the banks. It has a tufted woody root-stock like the Royal Fern, and in old specimens this may be very large and considerably elevated above the soil. Its erect lance-shaped fronds are

Prickly-Toothed Buckler-Fern.

X 156.

Wall Rue Spleenwort.

about three feet long, twice pinnate as are those of the
Royal Fern, yet presenting a very different appearance, for
the pinnæ are much more numerous and close together,
whilst the toothed pinnules almost overlap. The spore-
capsules are borne in circular heaps (*sori*) on the back of
the frond, each heap at first covered by a kidney-shaped
scale (*involucre*).

There is an equally abundant tufted species, often growing out of the rotted stumps that have been left when trees
have been felled. These at first get hollowed out by fungi,
then they fill with dead leaves, and when these have turned
to light vegetable mould, spores of the prickly-toothed
Buckler-fern (*Nephrodium spinulosum*) or its sub-species
the Broad Buckler (*Nephrodium dilatatum*) germinate, and
by and by the mouldering stump is hidden by the graceful
fern, whose rootlets penetrate into the rotting wood and so
are assured of moisture. Here the frond is much more
finely divided, the pinnæ rather wedge-shaped, and the
pinnules lobed, the lobes and teeth ending in spine-like
hairs. This specimen that we are about to photograph is
the typical form with nearly upright fronds, the lower part
of the stalk clothed lightly with dark-brown scales. That
one beyond with the broader and more arching fronds is
the Broad Buckler. They are among our most hardy ferns,
the fronds frequently remaining green all through the
winter.

As we reach the bottom of the glen we come again to
the bridge that crosses the torrent just before it enters the
river, and here we have opportunity for examining and
photographing another fern—this time one of the smallest
of them, though it is large when compared with the Filmy
ferns. This is the Wall-rue Spleenwort (*Asplenium ruta-
muraria*) which establishes its roots in the mortar of walls
and its root-stocks creep slightly among the moss. Without
close examination it would scarcely be accepted as a fern,
its small fronds being of a loose type of structure, the pinnæ

being attached to the rachis by comparatively long stalks, and the pinnules apparently stalked, though in their case it is only that their lower portions are much attenuated. The sori here are narrow-oblong; several on the back of the pinnule. Its name, of course, has been suggested by the superficial resemblance of its fronds to the leaves of Rue, so that it is usually referred to simply as the Wall Rue without any reference to its being a fern.

Another species of *Asplenium* of which we have passed

The River from the Park.

great numbers in the rocky banks, and growing from between the stones of roughly built boundary walls, is the Black Maidenhair Spleenwort (*Asplenium adiantum-nigrum*) which we may be permitted to shorten into Black Spleenwort, as it has no connection with *the* Maidenhair, a plant of another genus. Both its distinguishing names have reference to the character of the long wiry stalk, which is thin, purple, or black, and polished. The likeness to hair is not nearly so good as in *Adiantum*, for not even

Black Spleenwort.

a hog's bristles could be so thick as the stalks of Black
Spleenwort. Those of *Adiantum* are very much finer, whilst
the attachments of the wedge-shaped pinnules are really
hair-like in that species. However, if our forefathers had
been as matter-of-fact as our remarks may give the impression that we would have had them, we should have had
very few of the picturesque names they gave to plants.
One sometimes wishes we had a little of the imaginative
quality of our ancestors.

The specimen we have elected to photograph grows from
the bank, springing from a lump of rock that crops out
naturally. The fronds droop one over another with considerable grace, and regarded separately are seen to be of a
long wedge shape, of rather a leathery texture, deep green
and polished. The frond is very much divided, being twice
or thrice pinnate; that is to say, some of the lance-shaped
pinnæ are not merely divided into pinnules, but these are
subdivided into secondary pinnules. This is an exceedingly
plentiful species in some parts, considerable lengths of the
stone dykes having a plant in almost every fissure, and the
elegant fronds completely cover the wall. They do not all
arch over in the way of those we have just photographed.
Sometimes they spring upwards on very long stalks and
take an almost erect attitude, though there is always sufficient curvature to take off any tendency to stiffness. This
is a very disappointing fern for the collector who aims at
growing it. You may see him trying to extract an extra
fine specimen from a rock crevice where there is not sufficient space even to introduce finger and thumb. One after
the other the largest and toughest fronds are pulled at
gently but firmly; one after the other they let go their
connection with the root-stock; and the length of the stipes
shows that the root-stock is back nearly a foot in the crevice,
where it is doubtless rooted in fine vegetable mould and
probably only to be removed by pulling down the dyke or
digging out the rocks. And when he has succeeded in

getting a less admirable specimen from a less iron-bound situation, the probability is that the conditions of his suburban garden will not permit of his growing it—save for a short time, as an unhappy-looking starved plant that has scarcely any resemblance to its prosperous condition when he coveted it.

Whilst we have been talking we have gradually ascended to the upper road through the park, and the beautiful bridge and the village lie below, and the Nore goes winding away through the emerald meadows into the distant region of gold and purple where the sun has sunk behind the hills.

The Winding Nore.

Carline Thistle.

Rose-Hips and Bramble-Berries.

SEPTEMBER ON THE HEATH.

WE have not been on the Heath and in the Pine-woods
for some time, the light sandy soil upon which they
stand providing us with little in the way of flowers during
the hot months. They are chiefly attractive, then, for the
cool shade and scented air of the woods. In autumn and
winter when their soil is moister they have more variety
to offer us, though it may not be of flowers only.

We will approach the woods by way of the heath,
which is now all purple with the flowers of Fine-leaved
Heath (*Erica cinerea*) and Heather (*Calluna vulgaris*),
with here and there a patch of pink Centaury (*Erythræa
centaurea*) or a cluster of swaying Harebells (*Campanula
rotundifolia*). Quite naturally, you gravitate to the sand
pits, instinct telling you that is the moistest spot, and
therefore likely to furnish a few plants other than Heath,
Heather, or Furze. The crimson tint that attracts you
now is due to the leaves of the Sundews (*Drosera*

rotundifolia and *intermedia*). The inconspicuous flowers
have passed, and in their stead are the more noticeable
brown seed vessels. We are just too late, too, for another
plant of which we had desired to get a photograph. At
a little distance you might imagine that this plant, the
Bog Asphodel (*Narthecium ossifragum*) is still flowering,
for the red capsules are still wrapped in the orange segments
of the perianth, which are not quite large enough for the
purpose. Apart from flowers or fruit you might imagine
these plants to be merely seedlings of the Flag, for their
leaves are of the same sword-shape, though on a much
smaller scale. But they do not even belong to the Flag
family, their flowers being of quite another type: they
are in fact lilies, and very beautiful lilies, for they are
golden lilies. They were in flower last month, and in July
when our walks lay in other directions, so we missed them.

For the next three months the paramount attraction of
these woods will consist of fungi, of which they produce a
wonderful variety. They have started already, for about
the Birches here on the outskirts there are plenty of the
Fly Agaric (*Amanita muscarius*) and the Blusher
(*Amanita rubescens*) that we have met with and photographed before. But here is something new, though not
a fungus. Do you know this Carline Thistle (*Carlina
vulgaris*)? Although not one of the Thistles proper, it
is for its size more prickly than any *Carduus* or *Cnicus*.
There is not sufficient space anywhere to take hold of it
without having half-a-dozen fine needles run into your
flesh—leaves, stem, and flower-heads are alike protected,
and the spines point in every direction. It is only about
a couple of feet high, and the florets of which the head is
composed are purple like those of other thistles, but they
are few and inconspicuous. The most noticeable thing
about the plant is the circle of inner bracts to the head,
which are yellow and polished, so that they form a pale
golden halo round the head. The outer bracts, which are

Sloes.

very prickly, have fine filaments about them which look
as though small spiders had been running about them

Teasel Head.

and leaving fine strands of their silk behind them, or as
though the heads had been packed in cotton-wool. The

leaves are really lance-shaped, but so lobed and toothed, and every possible position having a spine set upon it, that it is not easy to see what is their true form. Here is a young plant whose stem is only just beginning to lengthen, and the whole plant from the root to the summit of the two big buds is not a couple of inches high, but these inner bracts glisten like gold and direct attention to the plant. The outer involucral bracts are green and leafy but well covered with spines, and an intermediate series is brown, reduced to branching spines, which form an admirable quick - set hedge around the buds. All these bracts and leaves are of a leathery texture, and retain their form long after the seeds are ripe. The dried flower-heads will act as an indication of the humidity of the air, for when it is dry the golden bracts spread open widely, and when it is damp they close up over the florets or fruits.

You ask what is the meaning of the name? Well, several explanations have been given, but the most accepted one, we think, is that which says the name is commemorative of Carl the Great, otherwise Charlemagne, who first used it medicinally, he having received private information of its virtues from an angel!

Speaking of prickles: here is a plant that is well protected in another fashion, for instead of spines like the finest of needles, this has short stout spines all over its stem and branches, and along the midrib of its leaves underneath. This is the Teasel (*Dipsacus sylvestris*), one of our most striking weeds, with broad leaves a foot long, and its numerous spiny heads swaying at a height of eight feet. Each of these plants began life as seedlings last year, and then presented a very different appearance. Here is a first year's plant—a mere rosette of leaves pressed close to the ground, but it is a huge rosette. In its second year it develops a ribbed stem, and the radical rosette disappears. The stem leaves are in pairs, with their bases attached in such fashion that the lower part of a pair forms a basin in which rain and dew collect, often to the amount of half-a-pint. Any creeping insect, that essays to climb the stem in order to reach the newer, tender leaves above, has his way barred at the beginning by one of these moats. Many of them, not realising that this is an insuperable obstacle, climb down the smooth inside of the basin, and perish by drowning. Just look into some of these lower

Cones and Leaves of Birch.

basins, and you will see that at the bottom of the clear water there is a thick deposit, among which you can trace fragments of the harder parts of insects, such as the wings and legs of flies, the legs and wing-covers of beetles. The soft parts have been dissolved. Some few years ago it was stated that the plant throws out filaments of protoplasm into these receptacles, and absorbs the fluid nutriment thus provided by the dissolved remains of its vanquished enemies. Knowing what we do of the artful

ways of plants, this statement caused us little surprise;
but a naked-eye examination of many Teasels has failed
to furnish us with corroboration; that is to say, we have
failed to find the absorbing filaments, which may be
microscopic. Our grandmothers could never have noticed
of what the deposit in these basins consisted, for they used
to collect this liquid as a face-wash to preserve their beauty;
and even to-day it is a rustic lotion for weak eyes! The
former use got the plant the name of Venus' Bath.

There can be no doubt, however, when we look at these
basins, and this liberal armament of spines, that the Teasel
knows well how to protect itself against enemies large and
small; for the spines on leaf and stem are obviously
intended for the discouragement of quadrupeds that might
otherwise be inclined to make a meal of it.

Just note how the main shoot of branch and stem ends
in a much larger flower-head than those surrounding it,
which have longer stalks. See also how some of the
involucral bracts—two especially—are drawn out to a
great length and end in sharp spines. These form a sort
of fence round the flower-head. Each one of the many
hundreds of flowers, too, has its own shorter bract which
is rigid and ends in a long spine, but all these are of equal
length. There is a cultivated form, the Fuller's Teasel
(*Dipsacus pilosus*), which has the tips of all these floral
bracts turned down, so as to transform them into hooks;
and this has made it an indispensable aid in the *fulling*
of cloth, no machinery having been invented that will
so satisfactorily raise the "nap."

The Teasel is a composite flower, although it is not
included in the Order *Compositæ*, but with the Scabious constitutes a separate order, *Dipsaceæ*. Every flower has a
properly formed, cup-shaped calyx, and a tubular corolla,
with four stamens and a thread-like style. In this head that
we have photographed you will observe that the open flowers
form a band about the middle of its length. Look around,

Yellow Boletus.

and you will see that some heads are in flower at the summit and base whilst the middle has lost its flowers. The head always expands in sections like this.

Some of the leaves of the Birch (*Betula verrucosa*) have begun to turn yellow, preliminary to their last flutter. Some indeed have already fallen, and make it easier to see the little oblong catkins under whose overlapping scales the fruits are concealed. Next month, as you stand beneath these trees, you may see what

Bramble Fruit.

will appear like swarms of little flies sailing from them to the earth on spreading wings. But if you catch one or two in your hand you will see that they are really little flattened shells containing the single seed, and with a pair of thin wings which give them the appearance of insects flying.

There are still a few flowers on the Bramble, though the bulk of the fruit is now fully formed and much of it is black, ripe and juicy. The village children are busy filling tin cans and baskets with succulent spoils of hedge and thicket. We fear that the fruit gathered on commons and woodlands will alone be eatable henceforth, for the hedges get so thickly coated now with the gritty dust raised in clouds by the too frequent motors, that the fruit from them will be no longer fit for use. It is, indeed, probable that much of our present roadside vegetation will be killed out altogether by the same causes. Such open spaces as this elevated tract of sandy heath will thus become more and more valuable as breathing places. Let us make the most of them and escape for a time from the vile atmosphere created by our automobocracy.

We called your attention the other day (*see* page 130) to the Field Thistle (*Cnicus arvensis*) which we were then unable to photograph on account of the wind, but here is a good-sized clump of it quite still, and the bees are swarming about its flower-heads, as well as large numbers of the slender beetles which boys call Soldiers, but which are known to coleopterists as *Telephorus fuscus*. A dark coloured species (*Telephorus rusticus*) is distinguished as the Sailor. Bearing in mind what we said about the differentiation of the sexes in this Common Thistle, you will see that the flower-heads of this clump are exclusively females.

Among the patches of Heath, where there is not so continuous a growth of it, you may find all sorts of things growing. These olive-green parchmenty stemless plants, that look like large Liverworts, and turn up their lobed margins to show the grey of their undersides, are Lichens. Each disk, which is two or three inches across, is a colony of low single-celled plants (*Algæ*), imprisoned by a fungus parasite. This one (*Peltigera canina*) once had a great reputation as a cure for hydrophobia ; hence the *canina* of its name ; and other lichens of similar habit have been extolled as cough-cures. One especially, *Sticta pulmonacea*, which grows upon the bark of oak trees and attains a large size, was pre-eminent as a remedy for lung complaints. We shall not meet with it

Sweet Chestnut.

Common Centaury.

in these woods, but if you come across it elsewhere you may know it by the underside having a raised meshwork pattern. This was supposed to resemble the structure of the lungs, therefore was it called Lungs of Oak, and confidently prescribed for all lung troubles.

Another of our summer flowers is still showing up here

Field Thistles.

and there upon the heath. This is the bright little Centaury (*Erythræa centaurium*), with cymes of neat pink flowers. We have met with it before, though we had not previously a good opportunity for securing its portrait, so we will take advantage of the present one. The funnel-shaped flowers, just now being visited by a Silver Y moth (*Plusia gamma*), vary in the length of their tubes and their styles, and there is a corresponding difference in the size of the pollen-grains,

II.—Z

evidently to facilitate cross-fertilisation. The anthers have an odd trick of twisting up as they discharge their pollen. It seems strange that this plant should not have been cultivated, for its general neatness, without any tendency to weediness, should make it a desirable addition to our garden annuals. Two or three exotics are occasionally found in rock-gardens, and there is no reason why our own hardy species should not be used where the soil is sandy.

The thickets of Blackthorn (*Prunus communis*) are well covered with Sloes, little black plums, whose blackness is hidden by a coating of so-called "bloom," which chemists tell us is a fine layer of wax, evidently secreted by the plant for the purpose of protecting the skin of the fruit until it is ripe. That condition has not been reached yet, though the Sloes look inviting enough. Try one, and you will find its juices so astringent that it will cause you to perform what boys describe as "making faces." Some of the country people have a very descriptive name for this fruit, "Winter Picks," which indicates that it cannot profitably be gathered until it has been touched by frost. This has the effect of partially drying up the juice and giving a more mealy character to the flesh, a condition that may be known by a puckering of the skin. At that stage the Sloe may be eaten; at first in the same fashion as one eats the first raw tomato; then, as the palate becomes accustomed to the novel experience, one rather enjoys it, and eats another, but always slowly and with considerable deliberation. The Blackthorn bears much more abundant fruit in some districts than it does in others, though it may flower equally well in both; and a bush or small tree well covered with Sloes is a fine sight. But the attractiveness of the fruit soon passes when it is gathered, for very slight handling is sufficient to remove the "bloom" to which its charm is almost entirely due.

Just on the edge of the Pine-woods there are considerable numbers of fungi in groups consisting of a score or more of individuals. They are not very attractive, for their caps

Nettle-Leaved Bellflower.

are coated with a thick brown slime—especially objectionable
after rain or dew; but as the plant gets older the slime gets
washed off, leaving the top paler. It is the Yellow Boletus
(*Boletus luteus*), so-called from the colour of the tubes and
the underside generally. It is one that is readily distin-

Centaury.

guished—though the same cannot be said of all *Boleti*—for
this is one of very few British species in which the stem is
ornamented by a broad white frill or ring, similar to what
we found in the Fly Agaric and the Blusher. The convex
cap is three or four inches across, and the stem is about the
same in length with a thickness of half an inch. It has a
whitish flesh that does not change its colour when cut or

broken, as happened with the Lurid Boletus (*see* p. 114).   The sliminess is not a prepossessing feature; but we can assure you that this having been washed off, and the tubes removed, it makes a very fine dish.   Indeed, there is no species of *Boletus* that we appreciate so much.

There are many other kinds of fungus in the woods, although this is only the beginning of the season, and we cannot stay long to-day to study them.   They are by no means all edible.   Here, for example, is one fashioned much like the Fly Agaric though of far more slender proportions, and of a yellowish-white colour with broad irregular scales on the flat top, white gills, and frill.   This is the *Amanita mappa*, and it is reputed to be a very poisonous species.

The ground under the trees is thickly carpeted with pine-needles, which are mostly bare; but, because of its bare brownness it shows up with greater distinctness the cushions of silvery moss that lie all over it, most of them loose upon the surface.   They are tufts of *Leucobryum glaucum*, and the habit of growing in such crowded cushions seems to have the effect of forcing the central portions out of the loose soil.

Beyond the outer belt of Pines we come upon more mixed wood, which includes a few Oaks and some fine Birches; but, over a considerable area, Sweet Chestnut (*Castanea sativa*) is the predominant tree.   Fine Chestnuts these are, too, and the large, boldly toothed, drooping leaves are of a rich green.   The hedgehog-like fruit is getting large, and we think we must expose a plate on one of those lower sprays.   There is a good deal of movement, not only lateral but vertical also; but there is a good top-light just here, that may yield us a good photo.   Strong though the outward resemblance of this fruit is to that of the Horse Chestnut, we need not tell you who know the flowers of both that there is no relationship between them; the similarity of the capsule has sufficed to suggest similar names.

The Sweet Chestnuts ripen here, but they never attain

Fumitory.

Spear Plume-Thistle.

their proper size. Come here in a month's time and you will find things fairly lively in this wood, for the prickly burs will be falling thickly and heavily all around and on you. We were photographing fungi here last autumn, when the Chestnuts were falling so incessantly that at length we had to beat a retreat, in fear that the camera-bellows would be punctured by them.

As we leave the Chestnut plantation and get among the tall pines again we cross a drain whose straight sides are beautifully draped with several species of Liverworts (*Marchantia*, etc.), and Mosses. Here and there is a young Hard Fern (*Lomaria spicant*), a plant that was plentiful in these woods ten years ago. There is little underwood here, the Pine canopy being so dense as to shut out the sun's rays. A few Brambles trail over the dry carpet of pine-needles, and where there is a moist hollow the sphagnum-moss covers it, and nourishes the Cross-leaved Heath. The Pine-roots run along the surface, and here and there they are ornamented by the huge *Polyporus schweinitzii* whose short stem supports a shaggy purple-brown cap eight or nine inches across. These are mature specimens; when younger the brown has a reddish tinge. The underside of the cap is a sponge-like layer of greenish-yellow tubes.

You are gazing at that heap of pine-needles, and wondering why they should have been swept up in that way here in the woods; but that is not the work of any human sweeper. It is the nest of the Wood Ant (*Formica rufa*), and if you look more closely at it, you will see plenty of the industrious insects hauling up little logs of wood to further augment its proportions. It is the largest of our native ants, and it has a special fondness for pine-woods. That heap of needles a couple of feet high is a huge city, and there are many entrances upon its flanks whence the polished deep-brown ants are constantly issuing on some important social business. Take care that you do not interfere with them, or your face will burn with the tiny jets of formic acid they will eject at you. No, we shall not photograph it. We have photographed several such nests, but the results are not encouraging. You see, if you could show all these ants coming and going, as we see them now, the photograph would be interesting; but the light here is so poor, and the subjects are so dark, that the necessary exposure gives you a picture of a heap of pine-needles and twigs without a trace of an ant. The hill keeps still, but the ants are not quiet for an instant.

A Pine-Wood Road.

Salad Burnet.

A Three-Went Way.

SEPTEMBER ON THE HILLS.

THE lane leading up the hill is getting overgrown, but
much of the vegetation is in the fruiting stage. The
upper parts of the hedges have been roughly trimmed back,
to prevent the abstraction of too much corn from the wains
on their way from the harvest fields to the rickyards. Even
so, they are liberally ornamented with straw. Herb Robert,
whose acquaintance we made quite early in our rambles,
still smiles at us from the hedge bank, its leaves and stems
redder than its flowers. Here and there a Spindle-tree
(*Euonymus europæus*) in the hedge hangs out its quaintly
shaped four-lobed fruits of pale crimson. Next month, when
the four lobes split open along these plainly marked lines
and disclose the four seeds each wrapped in an orange *aril*,
(like the *mace* of Nutmeg), these fruits become highly
ornamental and striking features of the hedgerow and wood-

side.   Like some other attractive fruits those of the Spindle
are reputed poisonous.

The Small-leaved Maple (*Acer campestre*), which is well-
represented in these hedges, is turning crimson and showing
abundance of its double "keys," or fruits.   There are plenty
of fruits, too, on Wild Rose and Hawthorn, which have now
attained nearly to full size, though the characteristic red has
not yet got its brightness.   At the hedge-bottom there are stiff,
short spikes crowded with bright red berries, that are the
successors of the greenish hoods of Cuckoo - pint we saw in the spring (*see* Plate 18, vol. i.).   Not a leaf, or other vestige, is left to show the connection be-tween the flowers and the berries, but we have watched their progress at inter-vals when hunt-ing below the hedge for other things.

Here on the bank is one of our finest, most im-posing of Wild F l o w e r s — t h e N e t t l e - leaved Bellflower (*Cam-panula trache-lium*), that until

Fruit of Spindle.

Marjoram.

recently has been masquerading as a Stinging Nettle after the manner of the White Dead Nettle. As it grows among the usual constituents of hedge-row vegetation it looks very nettle-like, but now, from the axils of the upper leaves and bracts of its three-feet stem, it sends out a few - flowered raceme of bell-shaped blue-purple flowers, their margins cut into five deep lobes and otherwise agreeing with the Harebell in structure. In speaking of that species we ventured to express a doubt that the hanging attitude of the flower was to prevent the deterioration of the honey by rain or dew entering the bell, and that doubt was based on our memory of the way in which the Nettle-leaved and the Broad-leaved (*Campanula latifolia*) Bell-flowers carry their blossoms. They also have honey to spoil, but apparently it is of so good a quality— so rich in sugar—that it will bear such watering as it may get. You will notice that though some of the bells are almost horizontal, the majority of them are more or less erect. The horizontal position is sometimes due to other causes than the natural tendency of the plant, for we have sometimes found the bells occupied at evening as dormitories by sleeping Humble-bees, whose weight caused the bell to incline upon its stalk. Whether these bees were homeless merely, or weary, overcome by their potations, we should not like to say.

It is rather late in the day to be calling special attention to the Fumitory (*Fumaria officinalis*), for it has been flowering in corn-fields and fallows since May, and is not yet over. This specimen we should judge, by its freshness, to be a kind of second edition, grown from one of this season's seeds. But late or early we shall not probably find a better example for photographing. It is usually so mixed up with other plants that it is difficult to show its small details in a photograph. This one is tolerably clear. The Fumitories are plants of very delicate texture and glaucous hue, reminding one of the more tender kinds of Ferns. The stems

II.—Aa

are quite weak and usually seek the support of other herbs. The leaves are much divided into narrow segments, and very thin. The purple flowers, which are borne in racemes, are rather singular. There are two small scale-like sepals and four unequal petals, the two outer being larger than the two inner ones, and all connected to form a tube, which is swollen at the base and darker at the tip. There are six stamens and a thread-like style. The fruits are little round nuts, each containing a single seed. This is regarded as not being a true native, but one of the hangers-on of husbandry that has migrated from the Continent, not only to Britain, but almost to all parts of the earth where the plough and the spade has made a way for it.

Well, here we are on the open common on the hillside, with choice of quiet turfy glades, deep woods, and breezy hilltop. We will visit each in turn, and see what they contain, if you will undertake only to do your nut-gathering and blackberry-picking whilst we are photographing. There is a distinct feeling of autumn in the air, a freshness that is delightful after the scorching heats of summer, and a sense of ripeness in the presence of the wild fruits and the mellowing tints of the foliage. There are

> " Calm and deep peace on this high wold,
>   And on these dews that drench the furze,
>   And all the silvery gossamers
>   That twinkle into green and gold."

There are some fine Thistles here, and they are now well in flower. This one, which from a single root forms a bush five feet through and quite as many in height, is the Spear Plume-thistle (*Cnicus lanceolatus*), a relation of the despised Field Thistle, but a far more beautiful one. Its stem branches from the base and at intervals higher up. It is usually a biennial, and in its first year has only radical leaves which form a large and spiny rosette, flat on the ground. After the stem has got well started, these radical leaves become absorbed and disappear. The stem-leaves

Rose of Sharon.

are not so fine, but they are strong, tough, and bold, pinnately cut into narrow triangular lobes, each ending in a spine, and the main portion of the leaf runs into a long spear with a fine hard spine for a point. The stems, too, are spiny, for they have expansions known as wings which

Head of Spear Plume-Thistle.

are pretty well all spines. The main shoot of each branch ends in one fine large flower-head, but the side shoots terminate in a little bunch of somewhat smaller, narrower heads. These flower-heads are the chief glory of the plant. They are egg-shaped and consist of a large number of spiny bracts arranged spirally. From the narrow upper end come out the crowded purple corollas of the florets, and form a soft brush. Now, we have photographed a small plant, or as much as we could accommodate upon our plate; but we will also have one of a single head, and it shall be one of those that terminate a central shoot. That should make a fine photo, for it shows the spiral arrangement of the bracts and their spinous tips. A few of the heads are already ripening their seeds, and the pappus or "thistle-down" is getting ready to spread its filaments and float the attached seed to fresh woods and pastures new. The pappus is really the calyx of the floret, and if you examine it with your pocket lens you will see that all its filaments —fine as they are—have yet finer branches on each side. They are thus like minute feathers. Folks in general have an impression that the name *Plume*-thistle has reference to the brush of purple florets; but that is not so—it marks the difference between the genus *Cnicus* and the genus *Carduus* whose pappus is not feathered.

Here is another Composite, but of very different aspect. You have no need to be told that it is the Chicory (*Cichorium intybus*) for we have no other blue flower at all like it. Roughly speaking, you may say that the flower-head is like a Dog Daisy turned blue, though, of course, the differences between them are very considerable, there being no disk-florets here. In the early summer you might have passed the plant for a Dandelion, the large radical leaves having a general resemblance; but the Chicory sends up a real stem, tough, angled, and grooved, which attains a height of three feet and puts out branches. The flower-heads have no stalks, and this gives a rather singular appearance to the plant; but it must be confessed that it makes a very fine show, now its bright blue flowers are freely out.

"What a strong smell of Cucumber!" you say. Although the Cucumber has been grown in this country for a trifle under six hundred years, we have never heard of its getting naturalised and growing wild like some other garden plants; and there are no fields around where it is grown. The source of the odour is under your feet, in

Stemless Thistle.

the pretty pinnate leaves of the Salad Burnet (*Poterium sanguisorba*). There is a large colony of it here, and most of the plants have gone to seed, but a few of the younger

plants are still in flower. The leaves remind you of those
of Meadow-sweet on a small scale. Do you notice that the
prettily cut leaflets are all stalked? Chew one or two, and
you will taste Cucumber as well as smelling it. Now you
understand the "Salad" part of its name, for it was formerly
used as a salad. But what do you make of the purplish
flowers? Ah! there's a bit of a puzzle for you. They
are really heads of flowers which have no petals, so it is
not very easy to make them out, and their small size adds
to the difficulty. The styles and stamens are the most
conspicuous organs. By pulling the head to pieces you
will discover top-shaped calyx-tubes, much like those of
Agrimony; and by the same token Salad Burnet is related
to Agrimony, and like it one of the Rose family.

For anybody to whom the Cucumber odour is objectionable, there is fragrance of a sweeter character just
ahead, for all those acres of the glade between the woods
are covered with the purple cymes of Marjoram (*Origanum
vulgare*), one of our sweet herbs. Like Mint and Thyme,
and Balm and Sage, it is a Labiate flower; and though the
individual flowers are small, this defect is compensated by
great numbers of them being clustered together. If you
examine the cymes you will see that the flowers are of
two forms, some being larger and of deeper colour than
others. The larger ones are perfect flowers with long
stamens; the smaller have no stamens. The anthers shed
their pollen before the stigmas are mature, so that cross-
fertilisation must take place. Marjoram is a plant that
has not got to be searched for; where it occurs it is in
such extensive communities that it can be seen and smelt
from a distance.

Another striking plant in flower just now is the Large-
flowered St. John's Wort, usually known as Rose of Sharon
(*Hypericum calycinum*), or Aaron's-beard. It is a native
of Southern Europe that has been naturalised here, but
some think that on these hills it may possibly be really

II. *Pl.* 91.   *AA* 183.

Purple Helleborine.

native. In many places it dies down in winter, but here
it is evergreen and keeps its large, handsome, leathery
leaves. Most of the St. John's Worts bear their small
flowers in large cymes; but as these flowers are three or
four inches across, they are mostly solitary. And what fine
flowers they are, with their soft golden petals and their
five big bunches of yellow stamens that constitute the
beard of Aaron! The *calycinum* of its name refers to the
large size of the unequal sepals, the outer ones being half
as large as the petals. After the petals have dropped off,
the ovary develops into a large egg-shaped capsule which
is sticky and has a strong odour of turpentine.

We have already shown you two beautiful Thistles;
here is another. No, you must not suppose that it has had
its stem cut off, and has put out a flower from the broken
base. This is the Stemless Thistle or Dwarf Plume-thistle
(*Cnicus acaulis*), and if you look around you will see that
there are plenty of specimens all alike in their stemless
condition. The solitary crimson flower-head, nestling at the
heart of the fine rosette of very spiny leaves, is a very
beautiful object. The prevailing idea of Thistles is derived,
of course, from the common species of the fields with its
dingy flowers, and the majority of people have no idea
that we have such beautiful species as this, the Spear-plume,
and another, which we may come across shortly.

And what do you think of this for an Orchid? Thought
the Orchids were all over, did you? This is one of the
later of them—the Purple Helleborine (*Epipactis purpur-
ata*), a sub-species of *E. latifolia*. In the type the flowers
are mostly green; here they are of a violet-purple tint, and
there are more than one of the three-feet stems springing
from the same root. It is one of the Orchids that have a
creeping root instead of tubers, a leafy stem, and it grows
in woods.

This shabby looking plant you would imagine to be long
past its prime, but in truth this specimen is now in full-flower.

It is the Ploughman's Spikenard (*Inula conyza*). It is one of the composite plants that, like the vulgar Groundsel, has relations with showy flower-heads, but has given up the production of large rays. Elecampane (*Inula helenium*), a rare species of the same genus, has bright yellow heads, three inches broad, with long slender rays. Here the rays are scarcely longer than the erect brown bracts of the involucre, and very inconspicuous, so that as soon as the head opens it looks as though its work was done. Its stem is three or four feet high, and its dull green leaves are wrinkled and downy. It has a peculiar odour when gathered, which is (or was) supposed to be objectionable to flies and fleas.

Ah! here is the other Thistle we hoped to show you—one that you might imagine was drooping for want of rain; but you will always find its open flower-head in that meek attitude. It is the Nodding or Musk - Thistle (*Carduus nutans*), and in our opinion it is the most beautiful of our Thistles, not merely on account of its drooping habit, but because of the rich colour and softness of the crimson florets. The head is a couple of inches across, on a spiny winged stem, that varies from two to four feet in height, sometimes more. The bracts have long awl-shaped spines which point in all directions, and are covered with cottony filaments. Here is a specimen with white florets. The flowers you will notice have an odour which has suggested the name Musk-thistle.

And here is yet another of the Bellflowers, a distinctly autumnal species that we shall find in plenty, now we have reached the open down. It is the Clustered Bell-flower (*Campanula glomerata*), with a downy leafy stem, a couple of feet high, ending in a crowded head of erect purple-blue bells, of which the central one is the first to open. It will be in flower all this month and the next. There is an Apple Snail (*Helix pomatia*) clinging to this flint at its root, and this will serve in the photograph to give some idea of the proportions of the plant.

Ploughman's Spikenard.

There is another plant here that there is danger of passing over as the Clustered Bell-flower, though its stems are shorter, and its flowers more purple. It is one of the Gentians, and is known as the Felwort (*Gentiana amarella*). You see it has a more slender tube than that of the Bell-flower, and rather funnel - shaped than bell-shaped; but all the same, where the Clustered Bell-flower is so plentiful there is great danger of passing this Gentian un-noticed.

Still another bell-shaped plant, but this time of vastly different character, for it is one of the mushrooms— the Magpie Mushroom (*Coprinus picaceus*), so called from its black and white colours. It is one of a tribe of mushrooms that no sooner attain their full size than they begin to melt. That process has just begun in the present specimen, and,

Nodding Thistle.

close by, you will see the remains of several others that have only part of the fragile stem left, whilst the black stain on

II.—Bʙ

the ground around denotes where the dissolved cap has gone. When this mushroom breaks through the earth it is more cylindrical in shape and pure white, but, as it expands, the white surface breaks up and shows patches of black between, a condition which has suggested the name Magpie. The spores covering the gills beneath are black, and, as the cap dissolves into a clear liquid, it carries these spores with it, so that as it drops from the edges of the cap the liquid looks like ink. We believe that some of the species have actually been used as ink, but some of them also make a very good ketchup. One species — the Maned Mushroom (*Coprinus comatus*), which is about three times the size of this, and is frequent among grass about rubbish heaps—is edible and preferably used for ketchup. Some of the smaller of these *Coprini* form great clumps with a hundred or more individuals in it. The Magpie will only be found in companies of four or five.

We believe we have already used the expression "one of our most beautiful flowers" several times, and we fear we must do so again, because there are many of them. We feel quite sure you will not dissent from our use of the formula in the case of the Hardheads or Matfellon (*Centaurea scabiosa*). Even from the point of view of foliage alone, it is a fine plant, although when it is in flower one sees little of its leaves, for they are mostly overgrown and hidden by other things. It is a perennial plant with a woody root-stock, from which in the spring arise the boldly divided leaves, a foot in length, with long oval lobes which give it great breadth. You will remember our finding the tall Broomrape some time ago, and our remarking then that this was the plant upon whose roots that particular form of Broomrape was parasitic. That was only a few miles away, but we have not found *Orobanche elatior* up here, though *Orobanche major* occurs on furze roots, and you can see its withered stems to-day if you look around. Hardheads is a composite plant closely related to the thistles, though it is quite without

Clustered Bell-Flower.

spines. Before its heads open they look much like thistle
heads without spines, but the purple flowers are very different.
The tubular central florets, indeed, are just like those of
thistle, but the outer row has been expressly set apart for
advertising purposes and contains neither stamens nor pistils.
In most com-
posite flowers
that have ray
florets the ex-
tra showiness
is achieved by
suppressing
the stamens
and using the
material for
making the
ray. But it
appears as
though this is
not sufficient
to make up
for the extra
material used
up in the fab-
rication of the
ray tubes of
Centaurea,
with their five
long lobes
around the

Magpie Mushroom.

mouth, which give the light and graceful appearance to the
whole head, so the ovary and style also have to be sacrificed.
The expanded heads are a couple of inches across. We have
met with a form in which they measured three inches, the
inner florets edged with pink, and the outer ones pure white.

Now is the season for berries, and there are many of them

around us, without mentioning the Blackberries which you have been well and wisely sampling. The Wayfaring-tree (*Viburnum lantana*), which we have watched from the unfolding of the leaves, and photographed in full flower, is now laden with masses of flattened beads of coral red which will soon turn to jet. Purging Buckthorn (*Rhamnus catharticus*) bears many juicy black berries; and every shoot of Privet (*Ligustrum vulgare*) ends in a great pyramidal cluster of small black berries. Here is a bush of Deadly Nightshade (*Atropa belladonna*), and it bears solitary berries, large, spherical, and shining black, set off by the large lobes of the calyx beneath each.

As we pass over the brow of the hill and commence to descend the steep chalk slopes by zigzag sheep-tracks, we find the ground well covered by a little plant that varies a good deal in height, probably according to the depth of soil, for much of these slopes are almost naked chalk—some only about six inches high, others a couple of feet. It is the strangely named Blue Fleabane (*Erigeron acre*), a plant with groundsel-like flower-heads of yellow and purple, but the latter is red-purple not blue-purple. Like those of Plough-man's Spikenard the florets are all erect and the rays are very inconspicuous. These are the florets that are purple; those of the disk are pale yellow. The plant has lance-shaped leaves, those of the stem much more slender than those from the roots.

You expressed the opinion that September was late in the season for an Orchid. Well, here is another, but it is the last of the tribe we shall meet with this year. It is the Autumnal Lady's Tresses (*Spiranthes autumnalis*), "autumnal" to distinguish it from the rare Summer Lady's Tresses (*Spiranthes æstivalis*), which flowers a month earlier. It is a singular orchid, in the fact that the leaves make their appearance after the flowers are out, and form a rosette to one side of the flower-spike. They are short, broad leaves of oval shape, and they spring from one of several egg-

Hardheads.